## "You're where you belong, Raine..."

Colston's expression was hard, the dark fringes of his lashes shielding any emotion in his eyes. "You're with a man you can't hurt the way you did Tim. And don't try to deny that you want me, darling," he went on. "A woman doesn't respond to a man the way you did just now unless she wants him to make love to her."

"If you think that, you're even more conceited and arrogant than I thought you were," she threw at him with eyes that flashed anger. He merely smiled, his hands moving over the ivory silk of her shoulders—sensual and arousing.

"We're going to be lovers, Raine. Make no mistake about that."

**Elizabeth Power** was once a legal secretary, but when the compulsion to write became too strong, she abandoned affidavits, wills and conveyances in favor of a literary career. Her husband, she says, is her best critic. And he's a good cook, too—often readily taking over the preparation of meals when her writing is in full flow. They live in a three-hundred-year-old English country estate cottage, surrounded by woodlands and wildlife. Who wouldn't be inspired to write?

## Books by Elizabeth Power

HARLEQUIN ROMANCE
2825—RUDE AWAKENING

HARLEQUIN PRESENTS
1078—SHADOW IN THE SUN

# Bitter Judgement
## Elizabeth Power

# Harlequin Books

TORONTO • NEW YORK • LONDON
AMSTERDAM • PARIS • SYDNEY • HAMBURG
STOCKHOLM • ATHENS • TOKYO • MILAN

by Mills & Boon Limited

ISBN 0-373-17030-0

Harlequin Romance first edition January 1989

Copyright © 1988 by Elizabeth Power.

# CHAPTER ONE

RAINE could sense the tension and excitement in the Channel Island office that morning, as soon as she pushed open the tinted-glass doors.

'There's been a massive shake-up in management at the weekend, Raine,' the blonde receptionist told her eagerly, filing a broken nail. 'The take-over's gone through and we've got a new MD. And is he something else . . . wow!'

Obviously Sheila approved of him, Raine deduced with a smile, unperturbed to discover that the new company had finally gained control. She'd been told it was on the cards when she'd taken the job.

'It's tough luck on you though, Raine,' Sheila went on from behind the desk, 'because they say he's got the drive of a power-piston, the ruthlessness of the devil, and on top of that he looks the type who won't stand any nonsense from anyone. And *you're* going to be working for him!'

'Thanks for the warning,' Raine laughed, with a toss of wild auburn curls, not allowing the younger girl's comments to worry her too much. Island Marine, she knew, had a good reputation here in Jersey, its marine development projects being both lucrative and sympathetic to the environment, and she considered she'd had enough secretarial experience to be able to handle its most difficult top personnel. Besides, she'd always worked best under pressure, she reflected.

She took the lift since it was waiting in reception—though normally she would have covered the three floors to her office on foot—and, humming a little tune to herself as she sometimes did when facing a challenge, she straightened the jacket of her green cotton suit before confidently opening her door.

And started, a cold, chilling sensation threading through her veins, a small, shocked gasp escaping her.

'Colt!'

The man was looking at something on her desk, a dark suit and immaculate white shirt adding to an elegance few men possessed, and when he looked up with those penetrating brown eyes registering initial shock, Raine shivered imperceptibly. Those strong, hard-hewn features would be branded on her mind's eye for life: the thick, rich tawny hair falling from a side parting over a high, intellectual forehead, the arrogant nose, prominent cheekbones and jawline, and the arresting sensuality of that firm, commanding mouth. But the years had added a hard set to the strong jaw—a grimness to already cynical lips—and his gaze met hers with such profound hatred that for a moment she wanted to turn and run. But she didn't. She had left Guernsey—come back here a week ago, she reminded herself firmly—not only to accept a position with far better prospects than any she could have looked forward to on her own island, but to lay all ghosts once and for all. And, if Colston Falloner still despised her for what had happened six years ago, that was his problem, not hers!

'Well, well,' he commented stonily, and the sheer loathing behind the deep, rich timbre of his voice made her shudder. He came to stand a yard or so in front of her, his cool assessment taking in the pale ivory of her skin, the small, freckled nose, full, perfectly shaped lips and the challenging glitter of eyes which were a deep, unusual emerald, and something leaped in his. 'Raine Welland.' He spoke her name as if it tasted foul on his tongue. 'Isn't it a small world?'

If he was shaken to see her there, he was concealing it well, only the whiteness around his mouth assuring her that he was doing his utmost to keep some powerful and dangerous emotion under control.

God! What quirk of fate—what cruel coincidence—had

decreed that *he*, of all people, should be the king pin of Island Marine? Raine wondered hopelessly. A man who, six years ago, had threatened to destroy her! But then he was so influential—had so many irons in the fire—that was it really so surprising?

'Colt, I . . .'

She didn't know what she had been about to say. Couldn't have said it if she had, because the dark intensity of his eyes held her speechless. With a chilling ruthlessness, that gaze seemed effectively to strip her of her hard-won confidence, her composure and, more disconcertingly, her clothes—moving insolently down over her full, high breasts, tiny waist and softly curving hips to the slender, provocative length of her legs in a deliberate attempt to embarrass.

She felt the colour suffuse her cheeks, the sheer impact of his masculinity unsettling. She had been aware of it before, but never so much as now when she faced that hard maturity in cold war, and, totally discomfited, she touched her tongue to her lips.

He noted the gesture. Noted, too, the tinge of colour high on her cheekbones, and his mouth curled in cold mockery as he savoured her discomfort.

'How many broken hearts have there been, Raine? How many . . . *lives* has that treacherous beauty been responsible for ruining since we last met? Two? Ten? Twenty?'

Clearly, he would never have believed her if she had told him that there had been no serious relationship for her since the bitter experience she had suffered with his half-brother, so she wasn't even going to try. Straightening, she brought her small, pointed chin up, determined not to be intimidated by his dominating height, or to let him shake the confidence she had found in giving her the courage to come back, and she said, surprisingly calmly, 'How many would you like me to say, Colt?'

A muscle pulled in the hard jaw and, as he took a step

towards her, she felt a nervous tightening in her stomach.

'You're quite a woman, aren't you?' he commented; and in the gaze that flicked contemptuously over her she recognised a fierce and elemental attraction of male for female. She was shocked when her pulse throbbed in answering response. A pull between two forces—like a pin to a magnet—that had nothing to do with mental reasoning, she urged herself to believe, and through numbed senses heard him say, 'You've really become something, Raine. I can't deny that. Though it was there, of course, six years ago . . . the embryo of that treacherous loveliness . . . even though you were barely more than a schoolgirl. But then you didn't have the confidence to go with it, to stay here and face me, did you, Raine?'

No, she reflected, her throat dry. It was that last meeting with him that had driven her away—a shy, timid eighteen-year-old, frightened and unnerved by him more than anything the papers had said about her—more than any of the gossip—more even than her own heartache. Under the light suit, she tensed, remembering the cruel shock, the pain, that had driven her to act as she had, the awful consequences, and afterwards Colt's visit—his grim determination to make her pay for what she had done.

'It *was* six years ago,' she stressed wearily, but the fatigued note in her voice sounded more like tired boredom, and despairingly she realised it when she saw how his mouth hardened.

'And that time lapse, of course, makes it easier on your conscience.'

The harshness of his tone brought that old, familiar fear of him crushingly alive in her, but for her own self-preservation she was determined not to let him see it. Green eyes glittering hotly, she retorted, 'I told you then, there were reasons . . . good reasons for what I did.'

Hostility flickered in the storm-dark depths of his eyes, an implacable hatred that had Raine licking her lips, and instinctively she took a step back.

'What reason was good enough for jilting my brother two weeks before his wedding?' he queried, with such cool restraint that a tremor ran through her. 'He was besotted with you and you knew it . . . yet you still walked out on him without a word. Cut him up so viciously that he didn't know what he was doing . . . didn't have control of that car.'

'That was hardly my fault,' she flung at him in defence. 'He——'

'Hardly your fault?' There was harsh scepticism in Colt's voice. He moved towards her, his hands resting against his lean hips so that his shirt was stretched tight across his chest, emphasising that dark triangle of hair beneath it, the superlative fitness of him in the play of hard muscle, in the narrow line of his waist. 'Tim swung into my drive that night so drunk because of you that he hit Stephanie's car head on, and you say it wasn't your fault? My dear faithless child,' he breathed, with such dangerous softness that she swallowed—hard, 'my wife is dead. My son's motherless. And my brother's scarred and crippled for life—all because you changed your fickle little mind! Have you ever considered how much suffering your little game caused to one family? Because it *was* just a game to you, wasn't it, Raine?'

'That's not true!' she shot back at him, the sun streaming in through the long-paned window making her hair shine like warm copper. 'And don't you think *I* suffered?' she exhaled incredulously, memory darkening her eyes. 'God! I regret what happened! Especially to . . . your wife.' She found it difficult to talk about, even now still finding it torturous to accept the cruel reality of what breaking off that engagement had led to. Yes, she had gone through her own personal agony afterwards—known immense guilt, though needlessly—but it was all in the past, and there was no way that Colt Falloner was going to intimidate her now. 'Of course I regret it,' she uttered emphatically. 'But I won't take responsibility for it,

Colt. I told you then, but you wouldn't listen. I broke off with Tim because I found out that he was seeing someone else.'

And nothing could have been more cruel, she thought, almost dispassionately now, than witnessing his infidelity first-hand. But, of course, it had been his word against hers . . .

The cynical mouth tightened and, unrelentingly, Colt said, 'Yes, you told me.' His breathing was shallow, and a vein pumped spasmodically in his neck. 'But you couldn't expect me to believe that, then or now.' He almost laughed the denial at her, though there was no humour in his eyes. 'Not least because of the way Tim reacted when he realised you weren't going to marry him. He denied the accusation and I believed him. Why shouldn't I, when he was so torn to pieces over you the way he was?' His eyes became two slits of hard, flickering steel. 'He was twenty-two and had his whole life ahead of him. Enjoyed sports. Squash. Cricket. Rugby. And now, because of you, it's as much as he can do to even walk!'

He had moved uncomfortably close to her, causing her to swallow again—her breasts rising sharply beneath her white, lace-edged blouse—and now, in his threatening orbit, she caught the fresh, masculine scent of his cologne.

'We've been through it all—six years ago, Colt,' she said quietly, the proximity of that hard, lean body making her mouth dry, her voice tremble a little. 'But, of course, you preferred to take Tim's side. Everyone did. If they hadn't . . .' She gave a small shrug, feigning nonchalance to give her the courage to face the heat of Colt's menacing hatred. 'It might have been his name that would have been dragged through the papers, not mine.'

Some sort of smile curled the hard mouth at that, and a spark of something lit the probing depths of his eyes. And very softly he said, 'But you still came back.'

Raine's gaze moved to the window which offered a view of the marina and, beyond it, the golden stretches of somnolent, sun-warmed beach that formed St Aubin's Bay. It was too early yet for the bulk of the tourists that flocked to the island each summer, so that there were only a few people basking there in the sun, and even fewer in the sea because the water was cold. It looked invitingly blue, though, the gentle, white-crested waves washing in and curling lazily back over the soft sand.

'Yes, I came back.' She faced him squarely now, her small chin held high, her back straight, trying to ignore the fact that, even in her high heels, she didn't even reach his jaw. 'Between you Falloners and the local scandalmongers you did a pretty good job of almost destroying my reputation.' She shivered, remembering how, as well as being cruelly hurt and disillusioned, she had also been afraid. 'But I was younger then . . . over-sensitive to what people thought about me. Now . . . I don't care. I've grown up a lot.'

A tawny eyebrow lifted cognisantly. 'And *that*,' he delivered coolly, 'is an understatement.'

There was a sensual undertone behind his words—an unmasked appreciation in his eyes that made her pulses quicken again. Her lips tightened—an unconscious gesture of rebellion against a primeval and very basic sexual attraction—and a hint of a smile touched his, almost as if he were aware of the conflicting emotions inside of her. Disconcertingly, his gaze rested on the mutinous line of her mouth before lifting to meet hers again. 'So . . . no forth-coming resignation?'

Raine took a deep breath, trying to hang on to her self-composure, trying not to let that shrewd brain of his guess at how much of a battle she was having with herself to stand here and face him like this. She knew she should have done as he was suggesting and resigned there and then. Left the island and gone as far away from Colt and his seething contempt as she could possibly get. But pride wouldn't let her. After fleeing from his threatening anger last time, it had been months before she had found the confidence to leave the sanctuary of her parents' farm again—to get a job beyond it—even on her native Guernsey. But she had, working her way through a succession of posts from pool-typist to personal secretary, eventually making a second bid for independence with her own flat. As before, she had found a need to break away from the stifling proximity of often rather over-protective, though well-meaning, parents. And she had studied, hard, furthering an already sound education with a full commercial grounding, until she was running the office of the large, though localised, components firm where she had worked for the past three years. And now that she had had the chance to come back here—earned the responsibility of a top PA with a fast-expanding, resourceful company like Island Marine—she didn't intend backing down.

'I've no intention of resigning,' she answered with soft resolve.

Colt's head inclined slightly and his mouth compressed, though his eyes were unfathomable as they bored into the soft green depths of hers. And he said quietly, 'Even though it's still my intention to break you?'

The ruthless determination in that cool announcement made the hairs rise on the back of her neck, but her gaze held his in stubborn challenge, and only the slightest tremor in her voice gave any indication of how much she feared him as she responded with, 'You can try, Colt.'

Anger flashed in the dark eyes but was quickly controlled, and his mouth curled in a sardonic smile. 'Not merely try, darling. Succeed.'

She would have made some swift retort, but he had moved too close, and the threatening proximity of his body, together with that faintly elusive scent of him, was robbing her of all coherent thought. A small sound escaped her as his hand slipped beneath the soft tumble of auburn curls, moving with breath-catching deliberation beneath the collar of her blouse, and he smiled with cruel satisfaction at the colour tingeing the pale ivory skin—the little pulse beating furiously in the exposed hollow of her throat.

'Afraid of me, Raine?'

She didn't answer, her tongue seeming to stick to the roof of her mouth, the dangerous stimulation of his cool fingers on her damp skin sending a charge like a volt of electricity through her, making every nerve leap sharply in response. Yes, she was afraid of him, but it was that dark sexuality of his that scared her most now.

'Colt . . .'

His smile widened as the small plea laced her voice, a gesture without any feeling behind it other than to hurt. 'Oh, don't worry, darling.' There was a cutting edge to the sensual richness of his voice. 'Unlike my brother's scars, yours won't be visible.'

If she had hoped that the years might have softened him, then she realised now that she had been under a gross misapprehension. There was a festering hatred behind that smooth, urbane veneer which time had somehow fuelled, so that his need to get even with her was like a raging furnace inside him. In panic, she pushed against him. She realised it was futile when he resisted with only a fraction of that impregnable strength, and he laughed softly when she dropped her hands to her sides, as if touching him had somehow burned her.

'When I'm ready, Raine.' His hand moved to encircle her throat and her breath locked in her chest, the gentle pressure of his thumb against the throbbing pulse becoming almost a pain. Yet some small, sick part of her recognised, with a wave of self-loathing, the stirring of a reckless excitement.

He watched the colour deepen on her skin, and must surely have felt the rapid increase in the betraying little pulse, because he was far too experienced not to identify a female's response to him. From the way his mouth quirked, he had. But then his hand fell away from her, and he said with a grazing harshness, 'If you think it's in my mind to dismiss you because of who you are, then think again,' answering a question that had remained unasked inside her. 'I'm going to bring you to your knees before I'll let you go this time, Raine, so the only way you'll be free to escape your punishment is to give up this job yourself. I doubt if you gave Tim as much of a chance as that.'

So he actually wanted the satisfaction of her own resignation? Was that what he was saying? Did he honestly think that his threats would send her running again? Or had he been cleverer than she had first supposed in putting that suggestion to her, guessing that it would only serve to strengthen her resolve to stay here? If he had, then he had assessed her nature well. Her chin lifted unconsciously, and if her nails were digging into her palms then he couldn't know it, she consoled herself, rising to his bait, to snap at him with foolish valour, 'Never!'

A muscle tugged in his jaw. Other than that, those strong features were inscrutable. He was about to say something, but the telephone shrilled loudly on her desk and, temporarily immobilised, Raine watched with guarded eyes as the man crossed the room to answer it himself, his movements fluid and easy, his body as lithe as an athlete's. She couldn't help her own body's rebellious tensing at the deep command in his voice as he spoke into the mouthpiece, any more than she could help noticing how long and dark his lashes were against the hard tan of his cheeks, how strong and sinewy his hands, and she almost hated herself for being so vibrantly aware of him.

In self-disgust she turned away, moving over to the window. A light wind was teasing the pink cherry blossoms along the tree-lined street, making the pavements appear as if they had been carpeted with confetti. She grimaced at the analogy, lifting her gaze to look out across the bay. Way off, a small yacht was bobbing about on the blue water, its white sails full-blown by the stronger sea breeze.

Like a plaything at the mercy of the elements—as vulnerable as she had been all those years before. Perhaps, in part, she had contributed to her own brutal hurt, she cogitated in retrospect, because in those days she had been so painfully naïve. But at least she had emerged from the experience with a shield—an emotional immunity against any further deep involvements with the opposite sex, a refusal to let anyone get that close to her.

Which was probably why she was so shaken now by that hard, male magnetism of Colt's. Pure inexperience, she assured herself, though admittedly, no man she had dated had ever exuded such an aura of devastating masculinity. And, if he knew the truth, then he'd never believe it. No one would, she thought, with a self-derisive twist to her lips, because almost it was laughable that, physically, she should still be as innocent now as she was at eighteen . . .

Looking up, she was startled to see him studying her, and his mouth was set in grim lines as he dropped the phone back on to its cradle. 'Does the thought of what you did to my family somehow amuse you?'

So he had detected that self-censuring little smile. She considered telling him that his family had been the furthest thing from her mind, but thought better of it. Privately, she struggled to bring some composure to her voice and won.

'You're making a big mistake with your accusations, Colt, but you're too narrow-minded to see it.' She turned to face him, her hands tucked inside the pockets of her suit. 'How you ever got to be such a big name in business with such blinkered vision, I'll never know.'

She could see by the way his eyes darkened that her remark had angered him. He looked about to say something, then caught his breath, as if changing his mind.

'Well, since you mention business, let's get on with it, shall we?' He swung a briefcase on to the desk, flicking it open to deposit a sheaf of papers inside. 'I've got a meeting with the

directors of my holding company, and I want you with me, so
we'll need the last year's accounts, records of outstanding debts
and all the take-over documents.'

He had changed the subject with a swiftness that left Raine
totally bemused for a few moments—unable to grasp that this
suddenly high-powered executive was the same man who a few
moments ago was promising revenge. But she was efficient
herself, and used to coping with split-minute decisions at top
management level, and seconds later she had secured the
relevant papers and was following him out to the lift.

'We'll take mine,' he advised in the car park when she
started towards her little green Fiat, and Raine felt a flutter of
nerves in her stomach.

Of course, it was simpler than taking two, but the thought of
being with him in such a confined space for any length of time
made her hands clench at her sides in trepidation.

One finely arched brow raised, she watched him open the
passenger door of a sleek, silver Mercedes and wondered, as he
closed it after her, how he could still retain that impeccable
courtesy—that unquestionable acceptance of her as a
woman—when her downfall was uppermost in his mind. But
if she had been worrying about what to say to him on that
journey, then her anxieties were unfounded, because almost at
once he was asking for a briefing of the last minutes of the
previous company, Marine Enterprises. Though she was new
to the firm herself, she was relieved that she could at least give
him that. Some time afterwards, she suspected that he had got
her talking solely to alleviate her tension and relax her before
the meeting, because he had the up-to-date information in his
briefcase, which he had obviously secured without her help.
She supposed she should have been grateful to him for that
consideration, if nothing else, but it merely made her hackles
rise to know how cleverly he could manipulate her.

The meeting went well. Taking notes for Colt, Raine wit-
nessed, with a reluctant admiration, the way he handled the

board members of the associate company, using both a hard decisiveness and a charm that was entirely unforced. But later, when they were alone and driving back to the office, he lapsed into a sullen silence, and Raine sat rigid, feeling awkward beside him, guessing that now he didn't need to manipulate her—relax her—for his own ends any more today, he obviously wasn't going to.

An adventurous toddler, too close to the roadside, was hurriedly scooped up by a scolding parent, which prompted her to ask, 'How's Sean?'

She felt, rather than saw, the hard glance he shot her way. 'Do you *care*?'

The deep, disparaging note in his voice chilled her. Of course she cared. True, she hadn't known the child well. But, on the few occasions in the past when Tim had taken her to his brother's home, she had enjoyed amusing herself with his baby nephew.

She looked strangely wistful as she glanced across the car's plush interior. 'I wouldn't have asked if I didn't, Colt,' she assured him guilelessly. 'I suppose he's been at school for a couple of years now.'

'About that.' The reply was clipped.

'Does he enjoy it?' she pressed, hoping to ease the tension between them by talking about simple, everyday things.

'He copes.' His eyes didn't leave the road as he swung the powerful car into a right-hand fork, and just as Raine was thinking, rather defeatedly, that that was the end of the subject, he said, 'He'd be a lot happier if we could spend more time together. At the moment he's living in England with his grandmother—attending school there. I've had to spend so much time away this year, and I don't like leaving him to childminders for any length of time. Consequently, I don't get to see him from one weekend to the next.' Raine noticed the rueful note in his voice as he talked about his son. Perhaps this was one way to get him speaking to her civilly at last, she hoped, her finely boned features attentive as Colt continued, 'He's a bright kid, but he still doesn't understand why he's got two homes while most of his playmates have one.'

'Wouldn't it make things easier if his grandmother came to live here?' It seemed the obvious solution to Raine.

'She's offered,' Colt was answering, 'but I know she prefers England, and I think it's hardly fair to expect her to uproot herself from her home and her friends—I wouldn't want her to. Anyway, I'm hoping to bring Sean back to the island as soon as I can.' And, in a voice that matched the car's menacing growl, he added, 'The boy needs a mother.'

Which *you* deprived him of, his tone assured her, more effectively than any words could have. Raine breathed a silent sigh of failure. So they were back to square one. He had no intention of letting her off the hook for a moment.

'Every child does,' she murmured, feeling sympathetic towards little Sean.

And wished she hadn't when Colt came back sneeringly with, 'A subject which you would know everything about, of course.'

His sarcasm made her feel as if she had brushed against nettles, and she started to say something, but he cut in, axing her attempt at retaliation.

'Some women are naturally maternal, Raine . . . they make good mothers. Others . . .' He brought the car out of a bend, his cursory glance at her taking in the soft curves of her figure, and his mouth pulled down one side. 'Others just use their feminine—attributes—to further their own ends.'

Plucking absently at the sleeve of her jacket, she sent him an icy look. 'Like me, naturally.'

He didn't answer, but his opinion of her was all too obvious.

He had taken the coast road, and so all his concentration was directed on the narrow, winding ribbon of tarmac, which offered breathtaking views of the rugged cliffs, a feature of the north. Some said it was the most spectacular part of the island,

and Raine had to agree. Pink thrift and white sea campions vied for brilliance along the rocks, while, higher up, tiny speedwell splashed sapphire among the verdant moss. The gorse was in full flower, too, stretching its golden blanket to the very edge of the craggy coast, while the cave-ridden cliffs loomed down upon soft sand and water so blue it looked as if it had been embellished by an over-zealous artist.

Her attention was brought sharply away from it, however, when Colt remarked, 'That dangerous beauty of yours fools most men, Raine, but it doesn't fool me. You're poison underneath, but it's so beautifully packaged that weaker men wind up like Tim because they can't resist those fatal charms. You convey that treacherous sexuality of yours without even having to try.' She looked at him quickly, amazed that he should be so aware of her—absurdly excited by it—but he didn't look at her, and his tone was flaying in its condemnation. 'Even those poor fools at that meeting this morning couldn't keep their eyes off you, so it was probably a lucky escape for them in assessing that you were already sleeping with me.'

His disparaging comments made her bristle, and angry colour scorched her cheeks. But she knew what he meant by that last remark. The indiscreet looks those board members had given her and Colt had left nothing to the imagination, bracketing them together in the most intimate way. But the mental images his words conjured up disconcerted her so much that she was throwing back at him,

'I couldn't think of a more sickening thought if I tried! And if everyone was as clever as you in reading minds, then they'd have known that you'd rather die than lay a finger on me, wouldn't they?'

In a voice so silky, so soft, that she didn't know whether she was hearing him properly, he said, 'On the contrary,' and suddenly he was pulling off the road and cutting the engine.

## CHAPTER TWO

BELOW them, a small, white beach nestled in the harbouring confines of a quiet cove, deserted, save for the interminable curl of the waves on the sand and a few scavenging gulls. Raine shot a quick look at Colt, her eyes wary.

'What are you doing?' she challenged, her voice husky with some guarded emotion which was making her blood race through her.

A smile, without warmth, touched Colt's mouth. 'Surely you don't need to ask, my treacherous child.' The seat squeaked beneath his weight as he shifted his position, the movement bringing him disturbingly close to her. 'Wasn't that an invitation?'

Raine's cheeks flamed. 'You know damn well it was nothing of the sort!' Her hand lifted to make contact with his arrogant features, but he caught it in mid-air, pushing her back against the soft leather with such palpable anger that she knew a raging regret in having attempted it.

'I wouldn't,' he exhaled heavily, his face so near hers that she could feel his warm breath on her skin. 'You should know better than anyone that outward appearances don't mean a thing, so take it from me—I'm no gentleman, Raine. I've never struck a woman in my life, but you use those vicious little talons on me and nothing will give me greater satisfaction than to *hit you back!*'

God, how he must hate her!

She winced from the pain his fingers were causing on her wrist, and he relaxed the pressure. She could almost smell the anger in him, but it was the force of that sexuality behind that harsh emotion which was suddenly rocking her senses, making her head swim.

His gaze fell to the pulse drumming fiercely in the hollow of her throat and he smiled. 'You know, sometimes in the past I used to wonder what we would be like together,' he shook her by saying then. 'Rather indecorous of me, don't you think?' He laughed softly at the shock his admission brought to her eyes, his darkening with self-contempt and a naked desire which he made no attempt to conceal. 'Oh, yes, you were the stuff of every man's dreams, even then,' he breathed with raw derision, a forefinger lightly tracing the soft curve of her jaw.

Raine tensed, the sensuality of his touch holding her captive—a victim of her own traitorous responses. Outside, a gull shrieked, its plaintive crying echoed by another, then in a squabbling chorus by the rest.

'Don't look so shocked,' he advised her with a velvety softness that might have been a lover's caress if she hadn't known how much he despised her. 'You might have been young and supposedly head over heels in love with Tim, but you weren't exactly oblivious to me, either.'

'You arrogant swine!' Sparks danced in her eyes, and this time her hand contacted the hard bone of his cheek before she had even realised it. Instinctively, she braced herself for the hard retaliation which never came. But she should have known, in spite of his threat, that he was a man too aware of his own strength to consider striking a woman, for whatever reason; least of all, for a simple display of hurt pride. Because that was all it was—an unwillingness to accept the truth. Because, infuriatingly, he was right. At eighteen, she had been dangerously aware of that raw sexuality, but it came as a shock to her to realise that he'd been conscious of the fact. The cognisance in those strong features stung more than any physical punishment he might have inflicted upon her.

'I've never been prone to delusions, Raine—either now or in the past—and at that party, when we had that innocent dance together, you were as taut as a violin string in my arms. Neither have I forgotten how you blushed when I looked down into those lovely green eyes, or how your heart pounded when I held you against me, any more than I've forgotten the way you tugged away from me afterwards as if I had the plague.'

And she'd thought that he hadn't noticed! Shame made her colour rise as she realised how naïve she had been, because of course he would have noticed. Even then, he was no callow youth. Her reaction to him was probably one he'd enjoyed from scores of women he'd held in his arms. But being married, and being Colt, that immense propriety of his wouldn't have let him make an issue of it. In fact, for the rest of the evening he'd treated her with a coolness that had bordered on positive indifference!

Heat suffused her body as she considered what he must have thought about her, because he couldn't have known how troubled she had been by the way she had felt in his arms. She had begged Tim to take her home early; tried to console herself that she was simply overawed by his brother's charm and influence; told herself that it was unimportant compared with the real feeling she had for him. But she could see now how that response to Colt could only have strengthened his ill opinion of her when she'd jilted his half-brother like that, out of the blue.

'You flatter yourself,' she managed to say somewhat casually, but there was a tremor in her voice which she knew hadn't escaped him.

'Hardly that,' he said coldly, and chancing a glance at him she noticed his inexorable expression—noticed, too, how the sun made his eyes appear amber-gold. 'So now it's down to just you and me.'

'What do you mean?' she queried cagily, her pale features turning to the hard bronze of his.

He didn't answer, but slid an arm across the back of her seat, and suddenly he was dipping his head to press warm lips against the pulsing hollow of her throat.

Raine sucked in her breath, her blood gushing in her ears, every cell screaming a response to the tender probing of his mouth—the fresh stimulating scent of him—so paralysed by his action that she couldn't even move to push him away. Even before she had recovered her senses he was lifting his head, his eyes dark and slumbrous as they looked down into hers.

'It's quite simple,' he said then, and in a voice as cool and emotionless as if he were ordering dinner. 'I want you, Raine. And I intend to have you.'

Her lids lifted sharply, the blood seeming to leave her veins. She uttered a small sound, something between a gasp and an incredulous little laugh, before responding, as cuttingly as she was able, 'And just how do you propose to achieve that?'

A muscle pulled at the corner of his mouth, and he pressed a button to open the electrically operated window on his side, the simple gesture showing how relaxed he was, how much in control, while her own heart was beating like the wings of a trapped bird against her ribcage.

'My dear girl,' he drawled, 'I'm sure that you, of all people, don't need any lessons in the art of seduction. And don't look so alarmed, sweet child,' he breathed softly, when she entertained the sudden, daunting vision of having to try and fight him off right there in the car. 'I've no intention of taking you here. It's much too cramped. And at my age I prefer the refinements of a bed when I'm making love.'

At his age? What was he? Thirty-six? Raine swung to face him, her eyes glitteringly bright. 'Love?' she sneered at him. 'You don't know the meaning of the word!'

She gasped as he gripped her shoulder, twisting her forcibly towards him. The skin was stretched tight across his cheek-bones, and his mouth was a thin line, showing how he was battling to keep his temper under control.

'That's rich, coming from you,' he exhaled through gritted teeth, his anger beating against her, consuming her like fire.

'Your kind wouldn't recognise love if it was handed to you gift-wrapped. You'd throw it right back in a man's face, just like you did to Tim.'

'I did nothing of the sort!' she shouted back in defence, totally intimidated by the bruising strength of his fingers, by what he might do. 'And what happened between your half-brother and me was nobody's business but ours, even if he did choose to spin a sob story to the first newspaperman who came to his bedside.' And, with a small plea which she couldn't contain, 'Why can't you leave me alone?'

As if that scrap of humility had released some of his anger, he let her go, although he was looking at her as if she were something that had crawled out of a waste-pipe. Vaguely, her senses registered the cool breeze from the window, the gentle wash of the sea.

'It becomes someone else's business when men ruin their lives—and other people's—over a girl like you,' she heard Colt saying with a steel hardness that was more unnerving even than his anger. 'You took everything my brother had to give you, right down to the last vestige of his self-respect,' he grated thickly, the glitter of hatred in his eyes silencing her when she made to protest. 'Well, now it's my turn to take, Raine,' he continued, deeply, his tone relentless, 'and—so help me!—you're going to give me everything you promised Tim, and more!'

She shivered, swallowing, and from his inexorable tone—his grim expression—she knew he wasn't talking about marriage. Nervously, she toyed with the hem of her skirt, the dark auburn curls falling over her shoulders as she stared down at the pale green fabric as if it weren't there.

'Don't you think I might just have something to say about that?' she retorted—but tremulously, colour stealing up her throat and into her cheeks simply from imagining herself naked in his arms. She was quite sure that he would know every rule in the book for tempting a woman into his bed—and for keeping her there. But she was angry to realise there was a tight knot of tension in her loins just from considering what it would be like to make love with him, and so she snapped, 'You can hardly make me go out with you if I don't want to!'

He merely laughed at that, and moved away from her to turn the ignition key so that the car purred into life.

'You can't,' she reiterated, when he had pulled back on to the road again, and she knew that he knew it, which was why he'd chosen to end the conversation at that point. Even so, a nauseating fear trickled through her with a self-debasing excitement at the thought of how he might use that dangerous magnetism of his to try and seduce her into bed with him. And though she tried telling herself that he was simply playing with her, browbeating her to see if she would back down and resign, all the way back to the office the voice of some deep-rooted instinct for survival warned her that men like Colston Falloner didn't make idle threats.

Shrugging off her fears with a visit to a friend's that evening, Raine was happy to discover that Colette Verbier hadn't changed a bit. Caught in her friend's welcoming arms, Raine knew instantly that Colette was still the same warm, ebullient girl who had been a firm flatmate and office colleague six years before, and neither had she changed in appearance. She was chic and petite as ever, bobbed hair—black as jet—still framing the small, pointed face, out of which a pair of baby-blue eyes twinkled mischievously.

'Ooh, it's great to see you, Raindrop!'

And she was still using that ridiculous pet name!

Raine laughed, returning her friend's hug. 'You, too,' she breathed, her anxieties over the things Colt had said to her in his car that morning diminishing under the warmth of Colette's greeting.

'And haven't you turned into something ravishing!' Colette was holding her at arm's length, studying Raine's eye-catching figure beneath the simple, white jersey dress. 'I always knew you were destined for great things, but heavens! God help the men on the island now!'

'You're too much!' Raine laughed, linking arms with her as they went inside, and feeling better than she had all day. 'How was England?' From regular correspondence with Colette, Raine knew that her friend had spent the past week on the mainland, and now she saw Colette's nose wrinkling disparagingly.

'Wet and windy . . . but Mum's happier there,' she commented, leading Raine upstairs into a beautifully furnished flat. 'She looks much more relaxed now than when she was living here with Dad.'

Colette's parents were in the throes of divorce and, since her mother was English and her father French, both had returned to their respective countries.

'But you prefer to stay here on your own?' Raine queried, sinking down, at her friend's suggestion, into the depths of a plush armchair.

'Wouldn't you?' One sweep of the dancing blue eyes embraced the opulence of the comfortable little flat, the thick brocade curtains, deep carpet and expensive, feminine touches. 'It comes with the boutique below,' she enlightened Raine before moving towards the kitchen to make coffee. 'That's mine, too.'

'You own it?' was Raine's astonished response. Colette hadn't mentioned that in her letters.

'It was a parting gift from Mum and Dad,' the other girl enlarged from the doorway. 'And all the furnishings. I think they wanted it to be their last joint present to me before they went their separate ways.' Colette sounded nonchalant about the whole thing. 'If they're happier apart, I suppose it's up to them,' Raine heard her say before she disappeared into the kitchen, and only then did she detect the wistful little note in her friend's voice.

Raine's heart went out to her. The Verbiers' marriage had been on the rocks for years, since Claude Verbier was something of a playboy, Colette had disclosed in one of her last letters, and Raine knew that her friend had spent a large part of her childhood torn between France and England during her parents' constant separations. It only made her realise how lucky she had been, herself, coming from such a stable and secure home.

'Seen anything of Tim since you've been back?' Colette asked, returning with a tray.

Wryly, Raine smiled, reminded of her friend's frank way of coming straight to the point. Of facing facts—however grim.

'No,' she answered quietly, her eyes trained on the plate of tempting assorted biscuits Colette was setting down on the coffee table. 'And I hope I never do.'

Straightening, the other girl shrugged, her white sweater and stylish orange skirt moulding themselves perfectly to her petite figure. 'It's a small island.'

Too small, Raine thought, shuddering, judging by the coincidence of finding herself working for Colt today.

'And don't tell me you're dieting, because I can't resist these!' Colette was admitting, scooping up a couple of the rather sinful-looking biscuits. 'Do have some. I won't feel so wicked if you do!'

Raine grinned, helping herself, refusing the sugar Colette handed her for her coffee from choice rather than because she needed to watch her weight. Fortunately, her height and the slender frame she had inherited from her father meant that she was lucky enough to eat whatever she liked without putting on a pound. Something of which Colette reminded her rather enviously now.

She was looking at Raine as if she had just seen a chrysalis turn into a butterfly and, sitting down opposite her, she said, 'If you do run into your ex, then it'll be his misfortune, not yours, because if he could see you now, girl, he'd kick himself.'

Raine gave her a small, twisted smile before sipping her coffee, endearingly reminded, by that last remark, of how loyal Colette had remained all those years ago when everyone else, it seemed, had been so ready to condemn her. But perhaps Colette knew, better than anyone, that there was more to a man than his charm.

'I'm the one who should be kicking myself,' said Raine, grimacing as she put her cup and saucer down with a small, hollow sound on the table, and briefly she enlightened Colette about the take-over by Island Marine, and the horrendous shock in finding out who was to be her boss.

Colette's dark eyebrows shot up under her fringe. 'Colston Falloner? The one who threatened to get even with you?' she whispered incredulously.

Raine nodded, remembering how, lonely and frightened as she had been by the man's threats six years ago, she had shared her fears with Colette.

'Oh, Raine . . . what rotten luck! Oh, well, he's bound to have mellowed a bit . . .' She broke off, her eyes widening as Raine shook her head. 'You mean, he's still stewing?' she asked, aghast, helping herself to another biscuit. And seeing the tension in Raine's finely boned features, she added, in a tone which was practical, weighing everything up, 'Well, what can he do?' She nibbled at the cream-filled wafer, brushing crumbs from her lap. 'Make your life difficult in the office? Overload you with work and keep tabs on you in case you're a second late coming in? Not that you ever will be, knowing you.' She grimaced, obviously recalling Raine's unfailing punctuality when they had worked together, a thing instilled in her by a somewhat strict upbringing. 'And he might try and fire you at the least opportunity, if that's in his mind for revenge,' Colette continued matter-of-factly, 'but he'd have to have a pretty hefty excuse, otherwise you could sue him for unfair dismissal, and that man's too clever, shrewd and level-headed to let his personal feelings interfere with his professional life.'

Which summed up Colt quite well, Raine thought with a little shiver, although she was surprised that Colette knew so much about him. She did manage a smile for her friend's attempt at consolation but, close as they were, she couldn't tell the other girl that it was her sexual humiliation he seemed bent on attaining—possibly because she still doubted whether his threats had any substance. Nevertheless, fear surfaced in her with some other basic emotion, to cause a tight knot in the pit of her stomach.

Noticing Colette looking at her rather curiously, she picked up her cup and saucer again, avoiding her friend's sharp eyes, and asked with a feigned calmness, 'How well do you know him?'

The other girl shrugged, her small frame looking rather lost in the deep luxury of the armchair. 'He moves in the same circles as some of Mum and Dad's friends. I got most of my information from them—Mum and Dad, that is.' Putting her own cup down on the table, she sat back again, slipping off her shoes and curling her legs under her. 'Apparently, he hasn't exactly led the life of a monk these past few years. They say he's been seen with every beautiful woman on the island. Mind you, he's a hell of a dynamic-looking guy, Raine,' she commented, as if the man's stunning physical attributes had only just struck her. 'I've seen pictures of him in the paper, and he looks more like Eve's answer to temptation than a wealthy business tycoon! All that charisma and male magnetism combined with that air of command!' She whistled softly under her breath. 'But he gets through more women in a year than other men get through hot dinners, and yet they say he was crazy about his wife. It's almost as if he wants to punish her for dying and leaving him like that. Oh, hell!' Bright colour spread across her cheeks and there was compunction in the blue eyes which met Raine's. 'That was unbelievably tactless of me. I'm sorry.'

Raine accepted her friend's apology with another little shiver. She didn't need reminding of how tragically Colt's wife had died. Hadn't *she* been held solely responsible? Neither did she need any assurance of his feelings for the fair-haired beauty he had married and so pointlessly lost. His grief-darkened eyes when he'd called on her that day, swearing revenge, had left her in no doubt about them, regardless of any claims he may have made today to harbouring thoughts about her, Raine. And he was still seeking that revenge . . .

An icy chill ran down her spine. So what did he intend to do? Make her one of his so-called 'women'? Use her and then discard her as casually as he believed she used and discarded members of *his* sex? But how could he, she wondered uneasily, unless he had her total capitulation? And he'd hardly have that if she made certain never to allow herself to be swayed by that startling sexuality of his, never to be alone with him, would he?

Half aware, she heard the clock on the shelf chiming nine, a thin, metallic sound that rang through her senses like a forlorn little voice—a futile plea against the relentless demands of destiny. Involuntarily, she shuddered.

'Have some more coffee.'

Colette's cool, practical tones broke through Raine's troubled thoughts, the safe, mundane action of coffee being poured dispelling her absurd foreboding. And after that they talked about the boutique, and Colette's plans for its future, and laughed over amusing times when they had worked together, so that by the time Raine drove home, her fears over Colt had almost entirely vanished.

The fact that he didn't come in the next morning helped further in allaying her worries. In fact, he rang in at nine o'clock sharp to tell her he would be away all day, and it was all Raine could do to keep the amusement out of her voice, remembering what Colette had said about him keeping tabs on her timekeeping. So he was going to try and plague her life in that way as well, was he? she thought. Well, let him! she decided rebelliously. She could handle anything the man cared to dish out!

She felt much more relaxed that evening, letting herself into her flat. It was more modestly furnished than Colette's, with its cottage-style suite and odd rugs scattered over the parquet floor, but it was home, and she liked it. And, after washing her hair, she curled up on one of the fireside chairs to watch a mid-evening film, although she switched it off half-way through because she'd lost interest in the plot. She had always been a discerning viewer, despite living alone, and instead she picked up a book—a biography of her favourite author—and went to bed.

She slept well, waking refreshed after a dreamless sleep to another bright spring day. In the tree beneath her window, a thrush sang—a clear, shrill song—and the lazy drone of a small plane broke the stillness of the morning as it passed over the clump of trees on the hill just visible from her window.

Downstairs, a chatty letter from her mother, telling her all was well at the farm, helped to lighten her spirits further, and she felt even better when, at the office, Colt rang in again to say he probably wouldn't be back until the following day. Consequently, left alone, Raine soared through her work with a speed and efficiency which even Jack Hardwicke—a retainer of the previous company and now Colt's right-hand man—remarked upon.

'If that lucky boss of yours finds he can do without you, then ask him to send you in to me,' he suggested, his face breaking into weathered lines beneath his balding head. 'You're ten times more capable than any computer, and a thousand times prettier, so if ever you fancy a change of master, I'm just next door.'

'She's giving her favours solely to me, Jack.'

Colt's voice behind them make Raine swing round, her heart beating a hard, irregular tattoo. So, he was back!

Numbly, she heard the other man laugh. Probably he thought Colt was being flippant, but the hidden message in his words hadn't escaped Raine.

*And I'll have them,* it had said, with a hard determination that brought a glitter of rebellion to her eyes.

His were raking over her in such a way that warm colour washed up her throat into her cheeks, and she was rather annoyed with herself for being glad that she had applied fresh lipstick and brushed her hair only minutes before he had come in. Why should that matter to her? she asked herself, piqued.

'Come into my office,' he commanded, exclusively to her.

She saw the older man slip unobtrusively away and, with nervous tension coiling in her stomach, Raine did as she was told.

He was wearing a light grey suit, the jacket slung casually over one shoulder, and as he stood aside to let her precede him she was very much aware of his body-heat beneath the fine, white shirt, the lingering traces of his cologne.

'What are you doing this evening?'

His question shook her, and it took her a few moments to regain her equilibrium. Did he really have the nerve to be asking her out? Really think she'd accept? Heat prickled along her spine and her Adam's apple worked nervously before she bluffed, thinking quickly, 'I've made arrangements.'

He stared down at her belligerent face from behind his desk now—a man very much in command, saying with a quiet insolence, 'Then break them.'

The dark amber gaze was tugging down over her blouse as if he wanted to rip the buttons from the prim, white cotton fabric. Angry with him—despising herself for the tingle of excitement such imagery produced in her—she said heatedly, 'If you think I'm going out with you tonight, tomorrow, or any other time, you can think again!'

Calmly, he dropped his jacket over the back of the deeply padded chair, clearly unperturbed by her little outburst, and one eyebrow lifted as he returned her hot gaze with positive disdain.

'I'm asking you to work overtime,' he exhaled in a voice thick with contempt, and as he strode over to take something out of the filing cabinet Raine felt her cheeks burning with embarrassment. She couldn't think of a thing to say, and when she heard the door click closed, rendering her alone with him, her knees went decidedly weak.

'Lesson one.' He was so close behind her that she could feel his breath fanning her cheek; she tried to move away from him, only to stumble over a pile of files on the floor, and felt the steadying strength of the arm which caught her. 'Never assume anything where I'm concerned, Raine,' he recommended deeply and with the self-assurance of a man who was used to winning. 'Although I'm sorry to disappoint you about tonight.'

His sheer audacity gave rise to a very sadistic desire in Raine to claw her fingernails down those arrogantly handsome features, and she had to catch her breath to stop herself making some pointless retort. But she had to salve her pride and, with her lashes fluttering provocatively, she allowed her gaze to move to the sensuous curve of his mouth—rest there—before saying simply, 'I think it's you who should be disappointed, Colt. After all, you're the one who can't seem to keep his hands off the woman who jilted his brother.'

She sensed every muscle in his body tense rigid. The ironlike grip on her arm became almost unbearably painful, and the condemnation in his eyes made her blood run cold. But then the harsh line of his mouth curled in a mocking smile, and his hand was lifting to the fiery strands at her temple, one cool finger moving down the smooth line of her cheek, making her heart stand still, her mind swim in chaos.

'Lesson number two,' he breathed, the silky softness of his voice seeming only to emphasise the dangerous anger he was holding in check. 'I'm not Timothy. And I'd advise you never to forget that for one moment.' And, his chest suddenly lifting heavily, he ground out, 'I'm not the fool he was, and I can't be taken in so easily, Raine. You use those little feminine tricks on me again, and you'll find yourself so far out of your depth that it'll be a pleasure watching you drown!'

Flushed, her breath coming quickly, Raine strove to find some cutting retort to throw at him, but he had swung away from her, back to the desk, muttering thickly, 'Now, let's get back to work.'

Her pride doubly stung, Raine decided that that was the best thing she could do. Colston Falloner hated her, and he wouldn't miss an opportunity to let her know it, she realised hopelessly, going back to her own office. It was mortifying enough that she'd made the mistake of assuming that he was asking her out. But to challenge him sexually like that! Her cheeks flamed as she thought about it now. She didn't know what had come over her. He was much too experienced—too threateningly male—for her to take him on in that way, and if she thought she could then she was asking for trouble, she warned herself admonishingly.

Plunging into typing a lengthy document regarding the take-over helped somewhat in easing her embarrassment, and in keeping her mind off the supercilious man in the next office. And though she worked late, she was relieved when he didn't once emerge from behind his closed door, so that she didn't have to speak to him again until she went in to put her completed work on his desk.

He looked up, obviously surprised that she had finished, a sudden complimentary remark from him about the speed of her typing sending an absurd pleasure through her.

'Are you ready to go?' His eyes took in the jacket and bag over Raine's arm before he dropped a glance to his watch, a gesture which brought her attention to the black strap spanning his wrist, the contrast of white cuff against bronze skin, the fine dark hairs on the back of his hand.

'Yes,' she murmured, without looking at him, feeling that too familiar tension building in her again.

'Come on, then. I'll walk you to your car.'

Now it was her turn to look surprised, her slender features querying the strong, hard structure of his as he got to his feet. And he said, 'I believe a young woman was mugged in the car park two weeks ago, so it's hardly safe for you to be walking around down there on your own now everyone else has gone. Besides,' and there was a satirical note in his voice, a hardening glint in his eyes, 'I'd hate to see anything happen to you before you've had a chance to clear your debts in full with me.'

Raine's head came up in an auburn blaze of staunch rebellion, her nostrils flaring as she struggled to keep herself from saying something she might afterwards regret. After that incident in his car, when she had slapped him, she was determined that he wouldn't provoke her into doing or saying anything that would give him the satisfaction of seeing her out of control again. Heading for the door, she said acidly, 'Thanks, but that won't be necessary.'

She was half-way through it before she realised that he was behind her, heard his, 'Well, I'm sorry, Raine, but I rather think it will.'

And so she had to suffer the humiliation of knowing that she had lost that round, though she didn't say a word to him, nor he to her, until they were on the wide sweep of tarmac behind the building.

'Thanks for working over,' he drawled, holding the door of her Fiat open as she settled herself inside. 'Now, go straight home like a good girl, and if you're entertaining a man tonight, do him a favour first. Warn him the nectar's poisonous.'

Slamming the door released some of the adrenalin pumping through her. Driving away from his arrogant figure with an unnecessary squeal of tyres helped, too. But all the way home she knew a bitter anger and resentment—had an overwhelming urge to ring him as soon as she got in and scream down the phone at him that she'd done nothing to deserve his continuing insults and his contempt. But she knew it was pointless even imagining that she could convince him of that—or even that he'd listen—and so, when she reached the flat, she donned a pair of shorts and a T-shirt and went for a soul-reviving jog instead.

# CHAPTER THREE

'YOU look tired,' Colt observed drily the next morning. 'Feeling off colour?'

Across the desk, his eyes were far too probing as they scanned the tense lines of her face, and Raine kept her gaze fixed on the notepad on her lap and the letter he had been dictating, reluctant to be exposed to that hard male scrutiny.

She couldn't tell him that she had been awake half the night, wondering why she had ever thought she could come back. Admittedly, she had been prepared that at some stage she might meet Colt again, but she hadn't reckoned on being plunged in at the deep end, having to work with him, any more than she had expected that hatred still to be so fiercely alive in him.

She had woken up with a headache which even her usual two cups of tea hadn't alleviated; and, after feeding a stray black and white cat that had wandered in through her kitchen window the night before, she had made the short drive to the office feeling as if there were a busy carpenter inside her head, letting his hammer fall heavily every time she thought about facing Colt.

What it all boiled down to, of course, was the fact that his threats were beginning to put a strain on her nerves, but she was determined not to let him know that. Looking up now, she said, with a small, careless lift of her shoulder, 'I had a pretty hard evening.'

Colt's mouth tightened, but he didn't say anything, nor did he need to. Those storm-dark eyes and the grim tautness of his jaw as he continued dictating assured her, without any doubt, exactly what opinion he had formed of her morals.

By mid-morning her headache was worse. Indeed, it had lodged itself firmly above her left eye, and she was beginning to feel sick.

Migraine! she thought despairingly, delving into her handbag for the pills she always carried for these occasions, hoping to get rid of the headache before it incapacitated her too much. But the tensions of the past three days had taken their toll, and within half an hour she was seeing the familiar flashing lights in front of her eyes, and had a head that felt as if it were about to burst. Switching off her typewriter, she dropped her face into her hand and groaned.

And that was the moment Colt chose to come out of his office.

'Come on,' he said, firmly, taking one look at her. 'You're going home.'

She wanted to protest, having the awful suspicion that he was going to take her himself. But she couldn't see properly, and felt so sick that she knew she couldn't have driven herself, so the only thing for her to do was comply.

He made her sit in reception while he brought the car round, for which she silently thanked him, and when they were on the road, he said discerningly, 'Do you get them often?'

So he was shrewd enough to realise what it was!

'No,' she answered heavily. 'But when I do . . .' She grimaced, wincing at the pain even that small shake of the head produced.

The quick glance Colt shot her way was censuring. 'I suggest you catch up on some sleep,' he recommended in a soft, yet disparaging tone that made her want to scream. So he still thought she'd spent last night entertaining some man!

She had a mind to tell him in no uncertain terms that *he* was the reason she hadn't slept well. That it was him and his menacing attitude towards her that was directly responsible for bringing on this headache, but she had too much pride for that. And now she was having to lose time at the office because of him. Damn him!

She closed her eyes against the harsh daylight, the pink granite houses and the stark white line on the road, grateful that Colt wasn't saying much, almost as if he sensed her need to be silent. Anything he did say during the journey only required a monosyllable from her, and from the absence of the usual sting in his words, it was obvious that he was going easy on her.

'If you need anything, call me,' he instructed when she was clambering out of the car, and she glanced back at him, met features that were less implacable today, yet still icily aloof.

'I'll be all right,' she uttered, deciding that she would rather die than summon help from him.

'I said call me.' It was an unmistakable command before he drove away, leaving Raine staring after him, realising that what she'd heard in his voice had come amazingly close to concern.

She spent the rest of the day in bed, and for a while couldn't sleep, her brain invaded by thoughts of the man who had brought her home.

There were totally different sides to him, she reflected, staring up at the ceiling. The one that was able to hate with an intensity that frightened her, and the one that gave her odd glimpses—like today—of his ability to care. Then there was that hard, male aggression which could so easily be channelled into sexual passion, making him, she was certain, a pretty incredible lover . . .

Thinking about such things did nothing to ease the throbbing in her head, because her body was pulsing with a fever all its own. Rashly, she pictured what Colt was intending: her own slim, ivory body crushed beneath the dark bronze of his in total surrender, the driving energy of his, her own impassioned cries.

Oh, God! she thought, sick less from her headache than her own ability to fantasise. I'm delirious! And, refusing to think any more about him, she turned over and eventually managed to sleep, waking around tea time to find her migraine gone and feeling remarkably ravenous.

Fixing herself a substantial meal, she then sat down to answer the letter from her mother, assuring a rather concerned Joan Welland that her daughter *was* getting enough to eat, and that she did have enough money to live on, restraining the urge to add that Jersey wasn't the other side of the world and that she *had* been coping alone for some time now. Then she went on to break the news that she was working for Colt Falloner, although she was careful not to let any suggestion of her own anxieties creep into the correspondence since, not wanting to worry her parents unnecessarily six years ago, she had never told them of his threats. After she had finished, she pinned up her hair, and went to run a deep, relaxing bath.

Emerging a little later, suitably refreshed, she wound a large white towel around herself and went to see if there was any sign of the cat.

It was parading up and down the kitchen counter, crying plaintively when it saw her. Scolding it gently for walking on the worktop, she scooped the animal up into her arms and hugged it affectionately, just as the doorbell rang.

She frowned, not expecting anyone, and with the cat still in her arms, proceeded to answer it.

'Colt!'

The name escaped her on a note of breathless surprise. He looked ultra-casual in a light, blouson-style jacket and dark blue trousers, and, recovering from her shock, Raine coloured, realising how *she* must look. Half naked, and with a half-wild cat in her arms!

His expression was inscrutable, but that dark gaze was scanning the loosely pinned hair and the smooth lines of her face—devoid of any make-up—moving down over the slim column of her throat and the black and white furry bundle she was clasping to her breasts, before his mouth pulled at the corners and he said, 'Since I had to pass your door, I thought I'd look in to see if you were feeling better. I've also arranged for someone to bring your car round later tonight.' His eyes were mocking. 'So there's no reason for you to be late for work in the morning.'

Raine stammered her thanks, assuring him that she was better, though completely ignoring his last comment, uncomfortably aware that she was wearing nothing but a towel. And then, as Colt moved, taking a step forward, the cat, probably misinterpreting his intentions, took fright, and with a wail of protest made a twisting, clawing scramble to be free. Raine winced as it shot away, then looked down at her hand and the three angry marks—red pin-pricks of blood appearing along each one.

'You'd better do something about that. Now!'

She heard Colt's concerned command, then the door being kicked closed. And, feeling strangely without a will of her own, she allowed him to lead her towards her tiny kitchen, wondering all the time not only how she had managed to let him get this far into her home, but also how she could be letting him order her around even on her own territory.

'Do you have any antiseptic?'

Raine nodded, gesturing towards the wall cupboard above the sink. While he was reaching up to get it, she put her hand under the running tap. Stupidly, she was trembling, and knew that it was more from seeing Colt than from any skirmish with the cat.

'Here.'

He took a still-folded white handkerchief out of his trouser pocket, tipping on some of the strong-smelling liquid and applying it to Raine's hand.

She caught her breath, not so much because it stung, but

because Colt had caught her hand firmly in his, because his own, personal scent was so stimulating, and because he was so close that, if she had bent her head, her hair would have brushed his jaw.

'Not your day, is it?' he commented drily, the mocking amber of his eyes meeting the lucid green of hers, and his sudden, cursory glance around him made her wonder what he thought of her home. His was a near-mansion, she remembered—in the beautiful north of the island—knowing from letters he had dictated that he still lived there. 'Where did it go?'

He meant the cat, and she gestured with her chin towards the little open window above the sink. There were droplets of water on the outside of the pane, and the swishing sound of a car passing made her realise that it had been raining for some time.

'It's a stray,' she explained, trying to sound casual, though her heart was thumping from this close contact with him, and she noted the merest lift of a tawny eyebrow.

'Do you normally adopt any likely waif that comes along?'

His tone was censuring and, as he bent his head, Raine tried not to notice how the lamp above them made his hair shine like hard, polished oak, how bronzed those hands were against the pale cream of her own skin.

'Only the four-legged kind,' she responded, with the smallest hint of sarcasm. 'And anyway, *it* adopted *me*.'

His mouth twisted wryly. 'Yes, I can believe that. I would imagine you hold a fascination for most things.'

Coming from anyone else it might have been a compliment, but his tone implied otherwise, and she chose to ignore it as he finished bathing her wound. Repocketing his handkerchief, he cast a glance over his shoulder, asking suddenly, 'Are you completely alone?'

The surprise with which he said it—intimating that he would have suspected the contrary—was disparaging, too, so that she was replying tartly, 'No, I've got a whole regiment in the bedroom!'

The trace of a smile played around his mouth. 'Possible. But I think that would take some doing, even for you,' he stated with biting cynicism, and that hard glint of hatred was back in his eyes. She tried to pull her hand free, but his tightened inexorably around her tender flesh and he laughed softly, so that every instinct of self-preservation screamed inside of her as he pulled her determinedly towards him.

'No, Colt . . .' Her eyes flashed a warning to his. Her pulses throbbed, and she put her hands up to hold him at bay. But her body was turning traitor, and little coils of tension were spiralling into aching desire through her loins as he bent his head to claim her mouth with the hard pressure of his own.

No man had ever kissed her like that in her life. Not even Timothy, during that farcical engagement, with his double-edged promises of undying love, had made her throb with such need. She gave a small moan, arching towards him so that he caught her to him with a fevered groan, plundering her mouth with a hunger that was as mutual as it was devastating, that knew only a craving to be satisfied as he pressed her hard against the long, lean solidity of his body.

His jacket was cool where it touched her skin, but beneath the towel her body seemed to be on fire, heat flooding her veins with sensations that made her weak. She slid her arms up around his neck, murmuring his name, catching her breath as his lips left hers to trail a line of burning kisses down the scented silk of her throat.

Somehow her hands had slipped beneath his jacket, her fingers luxuriating in the warm strength of him through the casual shirt, while his were moulding themselves to the soft contours of her body, caressing in a way that was as possessive as it was arousing.

'Colt . . .' She was lost beneath the touch of his hands, in the potent, masculine scent of him; that flare of attraction she'd known in his arms all those years ago was nothing compared with the earth-shattering desire which racked her now.

She heard him utter a small oath under his breath. Heard his husky, 'Good God! No wonder my brother lost his head over you!' And he was putting her away from him, his breathing coming heavily as he held her at arm's length. His eyes were dark and slumbrous, but his mouth was contorting with tangible contempt as he breathed, in a voice thick with accusation, 'What is it about you, Raine?'

There was a deep flush across the tanned forehead and cheekbones and, amazingly, she realised that he was battling for control. He had been fully in command of the situation until he had kissed her and then, incredibly, that cool, self-possession of his had been shattered by an inferno of desire for her that was as wild as hers had been for him. The knowledge of her own feminine power sent a reckless thrill through her, but it had only deepened Colt's hatred, she realised tremblingly now, if that self-loathing she'd heard in his voice and that fierce glare in his eyes were anything to go by.

Half afraid, she tried to twist away from him, but those strong hands wouldn't let her, pulling her back to him so that her own shot up to his chest in a self-protective gesture, registering the heavy thunder of his heart.

'You're where you belong, Raine . . . with a man you can't hurt the way you screwed up Tim.' His expression was hard, the dark fringes of his lashes shielding any emotion in his eyes, once again a man back in control. 'And don't try to deny that you want me, darling,' he humiliated her by saying when she would have offered some useless line of protest. 'A woman doesn't respond to a man the way you did just now unless she wants him to make love to her. If I had any doubts before I kissed you, you certainly dispelled all of those.'

So that was all it had been—an experiment to see how she would respond!

'If you think that, then you're even more conceited and

arrogant than I thought you were,' she threw at him with eyes that flashed anger, but he merely smiled, his hands moving over the ivory silk of her shoulders—sensual and arousing, despite her firm intentions to resist him—and she shuddered, her breath locking painfully in her lungs. Faint colour tinged her cheeks and she touched her tongue to her lips, as she noticed the cool, judicious smile which touched his.

'Perhaps,' he murmured phlegmatically, 'but your body betrays you,' which left Raine despising herself for her weakness in succumbing to that powerful sexuality.

Her pulses seemed to stop and then double their pace as his thumbs moved in light circles over the sensitive skin between her throat and shoulders, and beneath the towel her breasts ached their betraying need of his caress.

God, what sort of man is he who can do this to me? her mind clamoured, and she pressed her eyelids firmly shut, trying to blot out those strong, perfectly sculpted features, the high forehead, arrogant nose and cruel, sensual mouth, the thick tawny hair and the hard structure of cheek and jaw. She knew them by heart, it seemed, as every woman whom he had ever caressed would probably know them. But it was more than just the sight of him that she wanted to drive out of her mind. It was that subtle, arousing scent of him; the deep richness of his voice; that dangerous allure which added up to such immense, enthralling magnetism that she seemed doomed to become a slave to it.

'We're going to be lovers, Raine . . . make no mistake about that.'

The self-assurance in his voice reached every sense she had shuttered against him, and was all the more intimidating for being softly conveyed. So why was it having the effect of producing little frissons of excitement along her veins?

Her eyes opened in stark defiance, and met those which were dark with desire, yet uncompromising. Raine bit her lip, felt its trembling beneath the hard clamp of her teeth. 'Well,

I hope for your sake you live to be ninety,' she delivered, insurgently, 'because that's how long you're going to have to wait!'

He gave a low chuckle in his throat and, surprisingly, released her. 'We'll see.'

His soft rejoinder came with such inexorable resolve as he crossed to the door that Raine shivered. Would he be right? she was shocked to suddenly find herself querying. His coming here tonight had only shown her just how susceptible she was where he was concerned. But was her immunity to him so feeble that she could be ensnared by raw and primitive sensations which would eventually drag her into his bed? And when he only wanted revenge—to hurt her?

She heard the front door open, then close again, and she could have screamed, or cried, or thrown something, so great was her frustration. Colt Falloner had the totally wrong opinion of her and there was nothing—nothing at all—that she could do or say to him that would change his mind about her. Listening to his car pulling away, she wondered how this could be the same Colt who had entertained her with such amused indulgence when she was eighteen; who had stirred her to admiration with his brilliant brain and stimulating conversation, in spite of her being a little afraid of him, even then. Admittedly, even in those days she had thought her fiancé's brother a hard cynic, but that was nothing compared with now. The new Colt was cold and unapproachable, and bent on such a desire to hurt that it made her wonder just how much he might be suffering himself behind that cold, tough facade—what hard, inner agonies might be driving him.

Going into the bedroom, Raine knew a sudden, inexplicable tug of sympathy towards him. But no, men like Colt didn't engender sympathy in others, she found herself having to admit. They were much too independent. Too self-sufficient and self-assured to evoke pity. It was an emotion far more complex than that. And that was where the danger lay.

Pulling on a white silk bathrobe, she warned herself that any softening towards him on her part could only result in making her own subjugation easier for him. He had meant what he'd said. Her total surrender would be all he would settle for. And what *she* had to do was to make certain that he never had the opportunity to effect it—such as, not giving him any excuses to call round to her flat! Then she wouldn't be in any danger of laying herself open to that potent masculinity, or her own reckless response to it. Just as long as she kept out of his way . . .

The chance to do precisely that arose the following morning, when Jack came into the office with a proposition put forward by the new company chairman.

'Apparently, he's entertaining clients on the company yacht this evening, and sailing over to England with them in the morning. The only dilemma is . . .' Jack massaged his chin, something he seemed to do when he had a problem to solve '. . . he needs his secretary with him and Susan's gone down with 'flu. So he—er . . . suggested you.'

'Me?' Raine exclaimed, totally bemused. 'But this is only my second week . . .'

Jack's greying eyebrows lifted to a forehead that seemed to go on for ever. 'That's what I told him, but he said that, working for Colt, you're the only other person qualified to do the job—plus the fact that your shorthand and typing speeds are second to none. That's the trouble, Raine,' he grinned, with a little wink at her, 'your references are too good.'

She returned his smile, rather overwhelmed. She had entertained clients before: organised lunches and business conferences with the company where she had worked back home. But to be chosen to do so here, at Island Marine, when she hadn't been here five minutes—*and* on the company yacht! Her eyes sparkled like twin emeralds at the prospect. She had noticed a framed photograph of the vessel on the wall behind Colt's desk, and it was a sleek monster of a thing. 'Usually moored at Cannes,' he'd told her when she'd asked. So it was here in Jersey!

'What about . . .'

'Colt's already reluctantly agreed to spare you,' Jack was answering, prepared for what she had been about to say, 'so all I've got to do is ring our chairman back and tell him whether you've agreed to do it. It's a good day's cruise, by the way,' he enlarged, as if for added incentive. 'Sailing at dawn, with a flight back tomorrow night.'

He looked at her so appealingly that Raine had to laugh. 'You can tell him I'll be delighted,' she responded, knowing that it would make Jack's day. In the short time she'd been here, she had realised that Jack Hardwicke virtually lived to keep his superior management happy.

'You're a gem,' he beamed, going back to his office, but Raine knew her own pleasure outstripped his. She had always enjoyed personal involvement with clients, and the chairman's specific request for her services in helping him entertain was a boost her morale sorely needed. And, of course, it would mean time away from Colt.

She couldn't keep the relief out of her voice as she mentioned it to Colette in the street café that lunch time.

'You shouldn't let him get to you, Raine.' Colette looked up from the chocolate mousse she was tucking into, her expression concerned. 'As we said the other night, what can he do?'

Toying with a prawn salad she was having difficulty getting through, Raine smiled absently at Colette, who was finishing her creamy dessert. She'd probably starve herself for the next week to make up for it, Raine thought fondly, unable to understand why. Her friend looked perfect—chic as ever in a red and white fitted dress from her own boutique. Colour staining the skin across her cheekbones, she said quietly, 'He intends to get me into bed.'

Colette's mouth gaped, her spoon dropping into her glass

with a resounding little clatter. 'Ooh! So that explains why you're not eating properly.' She glanced up as someone passed. Around them, early tourists relaxed among the lunch-time locals; every table occupied, and the white fringes of the gaily coloured sun-umbrellas were dancing in a keen breeze. 'Just think of all that experience rolled up in that hunk of masculinity,' she suggested, turning back to Raine, and with an impish little grin, 'I could think of a worse fate!'

'Colette, the man *hates* me!' Raine emphasised with some impatience, her hair falling against her salmon-silk blouse like strands of twisted copper. Briefly, she explained Colt's precise attitude towards her ever since they had met on Monday. 'Granted, I can understand his feelings, to a degree. He blames me entirely for what happened to his family, and if I were in his shoes . . . I don't know . . . perhaps I'd feel the same way,' she found herself admitting. 'But that doesn't mean that I'm going to subject myself to the man's sexual abuse, no matter how dynamic he is.'

From the café, a man's singing drifted out—deep and strong —a French song from one of the waiters, happy with his lot.

'I don't think abuse is what he's got in mind, girl,' Colette cautioned, seriously now. 'From what you tell me, I think he plans to pleasure you senseless, then make his killing by leaving you flat. And he knows he's got enough charm and all the right physical qualifications to be able to succeed.' She leaned forward, her elbows on the table. 'If I were you, kid, I'd get the hell out while I still had some dignity to hang on to.'

Unbidden, Raine's traitorous pulses leaped to send fire licking along her veins, but her lips compressed in defiance. With a sigh, she gave up trying to finish her salad, and put down her knife and fork.

'Just now, you were virtually urging me into bed with him,' she reminded the other girl half admonishingly, her voice husky from the tumult of her emotions.

'Ah, good, coffee.'

There was a temporary lapse in their conversation as the young French waiter who had been singing brought the beverages they had ordered and went away again, though not before blowing Colette a surreptitious little kiss.

Both girls suppressed giggles. Colette had always attracted attention with her stylish clothes, dark features and big, blue eyes, Raine remembered, but she remained faithful to David Shaw, whom she had been dating for years. Despite his persistent proposals, though, there was still no sign of them getting engaged, and now Raine suspected that, perhaps because of the Verbiers' marriage being constantly on the rocks, Colette was probably afraid of settling down herself.

'Just now,' she was stressing, picking up the threads of their conversation, 'I got carried away by the sexual impact of a man I've only seen in the papers, that's all. But *you* work with him,' she emphasised, sipping her coffee, and Raine did likewise. It was hot and dark, with a blob of thick cream on top—a rich dairy produce for which the island was famed—and it smelt delicious. 'Also, you've only ever mentioned one or two boyfriends in your letters whom you came even remotely close to going steady with,' Colette was continuing. 'And if you're still the same person I knew, then you won't have been to bed with any one-night stands. That means you're nowhere near experienced enough to deal with a man like Colt Falloner. Whether he hates you or not, Raine, you're too aware of him for your own good, I can tell. Get away from him, that's my advice, or you'll wind up just being humiliated,' she warned in conclusion.

Raine hid her thoughts behind a wry smile, deciding Colette would be flabbergasted to realise just how inexperienced her friend was. Perhaps a strict, moral upbringing was difficult to shrug off but, even if it wasn't, Raine knew she could never have given herself lightly to any of the men she had known. She also knew Colette's advice was sound; even so, she couldn't give up her job. Anyway, for three days at least she wouldn't have to worry about Colston Falloner. Her immediate responsibility was to the new chairman and his clients on the yacht, and by the time she returned to Jersey the weekend would be upon them. Consequently, her excitement dispelled her other worries as she left the office early that afternoon on Colt's instructions, and went home to pack an overnight bag. She would need something special to wear for dinner on board, she realised, rummaging through her wardrobe and eventually deciding on a red cocktail dress with shoelace straps, which she packed with a few other items.

She had to be on the yacht by six-thirty—half an hour before sailing time, the chairman had told her over the telephone that afternoon. The vessel would anchor for dinner and the night in a bay off Alderney, the most northerly of the islands. It was a reasonably short drive to St Helier harbour where the yacht was waiting, and Raine utilised what time she had carefully, bathing and then washing and blow-drying her hair until it fell in soft waves around her shoulders, and finally pulling on a peplum-waisted, black and white silky suit which, she decided, would do for the following day.

About to leave, she put a saucer of milk outside the back door in case the cat should return, although she hadn't seen it since it had fled when Colt had called round last night. Perhaps, she thought, with an unaccountable little shiver, that feline instinct—more finely tuned than a human's—had sensed the fear in her, the imminent danger . . .

For a moment all her anxieties surfaced, putting a cloud on her horizon, but she shook them away determinedly. The immediate evening and the trip tomorrow promised to be enjoyable, and she had no intention of letting thoughts of Colt or his threats spoil it in any way.

Humming to herself as she stepped out on to St Helier harbour, she inhaled the bracing sea air, one hand shielding her eyes from the low evening sun which was shimmering across the water, making a proud silhouette of Elizabeth Castle in the distance. When the tide was out, it was possible to reach the fortification on foot by a causeway, but now it looked as if it were floating on the waves. And it made the perfect backdrop for the impressive, four-sailed vessel which had attracted a small crowd on the quay. With its sleek, white lines, towering rigging, and the sun striking dazzling reflections from its polished rail, the yacht was certainly a sight to behold, and Raine's stomach fluttered excitedly as she made her way towards it.

'Miss Welland?' A young, bearded crew member surveyed her with obvious masculine appreciation before welcoming her on board and without any preamble, was showing her courteously below.

Highly varnished teak and gleaming brass gave an immediate impression of opulence, as did the deeply padded seats in the luxurious saloon and the array of liquid refreshments in the boat's well-stocked cocktail bar. The doors leading to numerous cabins assured Raine that there would probably be room aboard to accommodate at least a dozen people, as well as the crew.

'Mr Cleevely hasn't arrived yet,' the man told her, showing her to her own cabin which had, as well as a comfortable-looking bed and fitted cupboards, its own private shower, she was pleased to notice. 'Neither have his clients, but I understand they're all driving down together. He'll be using the cabin next to yours.'

Raine thanked him, her face aglow with pleasure, and as soon as the man left she began unpacking her belongings, and changing for dinner.

Applying her make-up—a soft green shadow for her lids, a touch of mascara to enhance already long, curling lashes, and a red lip cream to match the dress—she wondered what the chairman would be like. When she had spoken to him over the phone he had sounded very amiable, quiet-voiced and elderly. Jack had confirmed it, telling her that the man also had a knack of putting everyone at ease.

Which would make for a pleasant trip, she thought, hearing someone entering the adjoining cabin, and wasn't too surprised when a few moments later its occupier knocked on her door.

Well, at least I'm ready! she thought a little nervously, answering the knock. And froze, riveted by the sight of the man standing in the companionway.

# CHAPTER FOUR

'W-WHAT are you doing here?'

Shocked, Raine was stammering like an adolescent as she stared up into the dark, daunting features, finding Colt's dominating presence unnerving in the narrow confines of the companionway.

A broad shoulder lifted. 'Cleevely couldn't make it.'

Raine looked at him aghast, the sudden motion of the boat stemming a fleeting and ridiculous urge to flee. 'You mean . . . you're here in his place?' He didn't answer, and she breathed accusingly, 'You arranged it!'

A thick eyebrow arched, and he shot her such a hard look that she decided not to press the point. He had arrived already dressed for dinner; a grey velvet jacket and bow tie, white shirt and dark grey trousers emphasising the sheer elegance of the man—that innate authority that singled him out from among other men as a leader. The thick hair was brushed back, those fiery highlights vying with the dark bronze of his skin and the richer clarity of his eyes, and for a moment Raine couldn't take hers off him. Then, recovering, she said tartly, 'Didn't the clients think it odd . . . when they'd been expecting our chairman, instead?'

'On the contrary, they seemed happy enough.'

Of course, they would be, common sense told her. Colt Falloner was a big name in the commercial world, carrying more influence than their softly spoken chairman who, Raine had learned, would be playing a far less prominent part than Colt in the running of Island Marine. The two men had probably decided that Colt's youth and power-packed energies would be more geared to securing a very important deal, and Raine knew that any client would be more than honoured to have Colt's personal interest in their affairs.

His eyes were appraising her through the clinging red silk, taking in the pale ivory of her throat and shoulders, the whisper of sensuality in the deep V of her dress, her full, high breasts. Warmth suffused her body at his blatant appreciation of her, so that she queried frostily, 'Is something wrong?' determined not to let him see how much he could unsettle her. 'I'd hate to be responsible for you losing a two-million-pound contract.' Which was what this trip was worth to him, she remembered, from a hasty perusal of the file that morning.

His gaze met the challenging glitter of hers, traced over the slightly turned-up nose, with its sprinkling of freckles, and the mutinous set to lips which were tantalisingly red, and he took a breath before his own compressed.

'If they're undecided at all about giving us their custom, then I'm sure just one look at you will sway them in our favour.' He grimaced. 'But then you're an expert at it, playing on that dangerous beauty, aren't you, Raine?' His voice bore the cutting edge of sharp steel, hardened by the momentary lapse of his self-possession a moment ago when he had caught his breath. He hated being out of control, she was beginning to realise, and just now when he'd looked at her—just as he had when he'd kissed her—he had been fighting an inner battle with himself because, crazy though it was in the circumstances, he wanted her! And to the point of obsession. She didn't need to be an expert in human nature to recognise that. 'You're a real *femme fatale*, darling,' he went on. 'Aphrodite, a Circe and a Jezebel all rolled into one beautiful package that, for some reason which escapes me, seems to drive men to distraction.' His tone condemned, and yet his eyes burned with a fierce, unveiled hunger for her that made her tremble.

Even so, it made her feel good to know that she could shake that impregnable masculinity, and a spark of challenge leaped in her, brought her tongue provocatively over her top lip, and made her surprise even herself as she responded tauntingly, 'But not you, Colt?'

Beneath the pure silk of his shirt his muscles flexed and deeply, unrelentingly, he exhaled, 'No, not me, Raine.'

It was a lie, and they both knew it.

Fortunately, the evening proved interesting enough to keep her mind off him. Dinner, provided by the yacht's own catering staff, was delicious—lobster thermidor and a dry white wine, followed by entrecôte steak, profiteroles and champagne. When Island Marine entertained, they did it in style, Raine thought, with a mental grimace. And how Colt could charm!

Once again, she found herself admiring his clever handling of a situation and people—commanding it without anyone realising that they were being totally guided by him, charming without any affected sincerity. Resentful, yet enthralled, she watched top executives from the client company succumb to his wit, his directness and his brilliance, the one female guest among them being no exception.

Jocelyn Day was the sister of one of the directors and, as far as Raine could gather, had come along merely for the trip. If Colt had thought that *she* could sway the men's decision at all, then they must have assumed that bringing Jocelyn along might grant them more favourable terms with the new magnate of Island Marine, because the woman, about thirty, was positively stunning. Slim, dark-haired, and wearing a slinky white dress, cut so low it left nothing to the imagination, she seemed content to let her smouldering grey eyes feast unashamedly on Colt for the whole duration of dinner.

'Are you a pure islander?'

Her question, aimed directly across the table at Raine, surprised her. She had been watching the last silver streaks of the sunset on the water through the low, oblong window, but now she dragged her mind back to the table and nodded, wondering why the woman had suddenly condescended to speak to her. Until then, she had been treating Raine as if she weren't there!

'Quite unlike Colt.' The woman's smile was for him alone, the light pressure of scarlet-tipped fingers on his sleeve as intimate as the way she purred his name. 'An intellect like that could hardly have come out of forty-five square miles of tomato-growing country. It would have been far too confining for its potential.'

Meaning that all islanders were imbeciles! Inwardly, Raine fumed at the deliberate gibe and the derogatory way in which Jocelyn had described Jersey. She would have made some suitable retort, but diplomacy held it in check. The customer was always right, after all.

'The island has a lot going for it,' she heard Colt's deep voice reasoning. 'Why else would I have left the temptations of a modern London, if it hadn't?' There was cynicism in his remark, but it was lost on Jocelyn.

'For a tax haven, surely . . .' Her words tailed off, amazement etching the beautiful face at Colt's brief denial. And then she was adding, with what Raine realised was another dig at her, 'I wouldn't have thought anyone in their right mind would actually *want* to live there. I mean . . . what has it *got?*' This with an affected little laugh.

Raine couldn't have resisted saying something then, but Colt was answering before she could. 'A history that goes back over a thousand years. A freedom from the pressures of every-day life in the mainland cities. An Anglo-French unity that exists in any street you happen to find yourself, despite remaining totally British and,' with a twist of a smile, 'it also has claim to the oldest Chamber of Commerce in the English-speaking world.'

A shiver of pride ran through Raine. She looked up, met the unguarded sincerity in his eyes, and realised that he loved the place he had made his home as much as she did. Silently, she was grateful to him for defending her island.

'She also bears the scars of battle . . . determined conquerors,' he was going on to add to a suddenly captive audience. 'But I think her culture has been enriched in the process, and I'm sure she's learned valuable lessons from her surrender.'

The remark was double-edged, and Raine couldn't look at him, the heat of his gaze on her making her aware of a fundamentally animal urge in him to conquer which was older than these islands. She was shocked to recognise an answering and primeval instinct in herself to submit, to give herself up to him as these lands had given themselves up to those first, early conquerors who had plundered their virgin soils and made them yield to their will.

She could feel herself growing hot beneath the penetrating clarity of his eyes, and beside him she heard Jocelyn's awkward little cough, as if she had sensed something too personal for her to share any part in and didn't like it.

'That's told you, Jocelyn,' her brother, who was sitting next to Raine, remarked drily. He was younger than his sister, but with the same dark hair and grey eyes, and he had had a leaning towards Raine that had been apparent to her ever since they had started dinner. 'The island's also been keeping other attractions very much to itself.' The smile he sent her way was warm and somehow boyish. 'If they're all like you, perhaps that's the real reason Mr Falloner lives here.' He sounded a little unsure of himself suddenly, and Raine saw him swallow, as if he was a little in awe of Colt and was wondering whether he had been too presumptuous in making that last remark. She could have kicked him for his fawning attitude towards the man, and from the other side of the table heard Jocelyn's tight, high-pitched laugh.

'Colt was married when he came here, Andrew . . . to my best friend.' There was a proprietorial note in the way she said that, as if the fact somehow gave her claim to the man, and she flashed Colt a smile that was blatantly inviting. 'I used to think you brought her here to hide her away from the rest of the world, Colt. To keep her all to yourself. I can't tell you enough how devastated we all were by—'

'Yes, all right!' His swift interruption was low and clipped, but that hard mask of self-command gave no indication of any pain he might still feel inside. There was only a cold accusation in his eyes as they met Raine's.

She shivered. So Jocelyn had known the Falloners a long time. The name of Raine Welland, though, didn't seem to be jogging any memory with her, and Raine breathed silent relief. It was probably only the island newspapers that had reported that story six years ago, so that possibly no one on the mainland knew about the thoughtless teenager who had wreaked such tragedy and grief upon the wealthy Falloner family. Except that she hadn't! Oh, God, she hadn't!

The horror of that time came back to her vividly—the desolation and innocent suffering, the press reports—bringing a cold clamminess to her hands. It was all in the past, she tried reminding herself—people forgot. And, dear God! she wanted to. But how could she, when Colt refused to let her? When his hatred was still beating against her? She could feel it now behind that exquisite charm of his, that cool smile and that strong, compelling magnetism that made him as dangerous to her as his hostility. Suddenly, she had had enough.

The others were talking, unaware of her inner turmoil. One elderly, bald-headed man was making some quip about cricket; another had lit a cigar. And Andrew was listening obsequiously to Colt, who was discussing some aspect of the island's legal structure, while Jocelyn clung possessively to his arm. There would be no more business tonight.

Excusing herself, Raine felt Colt's questioning glance as she stood up, was aware of Andrew's sudden, unveiled disappointment, but she ignored them both, glad at last to get out of the dining-room—to be alone.

On deck, the air was cool, and a fresh breeze stirred her hair as she leaned against the rail, looking seawards. It was almost dark and, anchored as they were in the small bay, Alderney rose behind them like a dusky haven. Eight miles to the east lay France and the Cherbourg Peninsula—visible on a clear day, but enveloped now by the encroaching night—and the intermittent flashing from a lighthouse broke through the gathering dusk, warning sailors of the dangers of The Casquets, a treacherous reef of rocks off to the west.

Raine took lungfuls of the damp, salty air, relaxing with the night sounds—the ripple of waves against the hull, the creak of wood and clink of metal on the rigging, and, filtering up with little pools of light from below deck, the murmur of muted conversation.

Hearing a soft footfall behind her, she turned, for some reason half expecting to see Andrew. Her pulses quickened when she realised that it was Colt.

'What's wrong, Raine?' His strong features were crossed with shadows in the dim light of the deck, but his voice was laced with hard derision. 'Was the conversation getting too uncomfortable for you?'

Raine tensed, biting her lip, refusing to be provoked into angry retaliation by his caustic remark. Instead, she took a deep breath and said casually, much too casually, she realised afterwards, 'No. Should it have been?'

It hadn't been her intention to antagonise him, but she had, and she felt the cruel lash of his anger as he swung her to face him.

'If there was any compassion—any conscience—behind that lovely face of yours, it would have,' he ground out, and now she could see the scorn in his eyes, the cold, simmering resentment. His mouth pulled down grimly, but he let go of her, exhaling a long, hard breath that communicated something like pain.

He was hurting inside, she was certain of that, and knew a

sudden, desperate urge to comfort him, to win his good opinion of her, make him see that she wasn't the fickle, uncaring creature he believed her to be. Almost without thinking she was lifting a hand to his arm, feeling the velvet of his sleeve as a soft sensuality beneath her fingers.

'You've got it all wrong about me, Colt.' Her gaze lifted, locked with his, and the implacable strength in those dark depths made her heart race. She gave a little gasp as his hand came down on hers, his fingers encircling the delicate structure with painful tenacity.

'The plea of the guilty about to be condemned?' His smile was cynical. Slowly, he drew her towards him, gently, but with a determination that brooked no resistance, and Raine held her breath, every nerve-end screaming her soul-shattering awareness of him.

The wind lifted his hair as he pressed her hand, palm upwards to his lips, their warmth firing sensations through her blood, so that she trembled. The trembling increased when he turned her hand over and let his tongue trace a sensual path over the still very apparent claw marks, the gesture giving rise to the fancy of the beautiful male predator licking the wounds of its mate. Above her fear of him, that sick desire stirred in Raine's loins. Way off, the lighthouse signalled its warning, evoking alarm signals in her of the danger—the devastation to her senses and her self-respect—which lay in succumbing to that treacherous tide of feeling. She tried to pull away from him, but couldn't, and panic lit her eyes when she heard the low chuckle in his throat.

'I promised I wouldn't mark that lovely body, and I meant it,' he breathed, his tongue playing with her fingers, the moist warmth of him sending a flame licking along her veins. 'So what are you afraid of? The inevitability of our making love? Or the fact that you might just enjoy it when the time actually comes?'

Her mouth went dry. She tried in vain to tug away from

him, fear leaping through her when she saw the implacable determination in his face. And suddenly he was releasing her.

'Go back to your guests, Raine.'

His cold command sounded more like an ultimatum, and she obeyed without argument.

Raine woke with a threatening migraine which she accepted at once as a penalty for indulging in wine and chocolate sauce—two things she was usually careful to avoid.

That's all I need! she thought, groaning as she threw back the bedcovers and, finding her tablets, made her way to the galley to get a glass of water. From there, she saw the first rays of sunrise breaking on the water and heard movement on deck. The crew, no doubt, raising the sails, she decided, as they were sailing at dawn. But there was no sound below, other than the quiet lapping of the water outside and, tripping silently back to her cabin, Raine slipped into bed, hoping that the tablets would soon take effect.

They must have because a sound woke her, and a glance at her watch beside the bed showed her that twenty minutes had elapsed. The sound came again—a soft tap on her door—and she looked up as it opened fractionally, then fully, when the man saw that she was awake.

'I was working and heard you get up,' Colt said quietly, coming in. He was almost fully dressed in dark trousers and a tailored white shirt which was casually buttoned, and Raine's stomach did a little flip. 'You left these in the galley.' He handed her a bottle which she recognised as her migraine tablets. 'I thought you might be suffering and would probably appreciate a cup of coffee.'

'Thanks.' Raine took both, giving him a half-appreciative, half-embarrassed smile, wondering wryly what she must look like.

The sun had risen higher and the yacht was underway now, the shriek of gulls above promising to accompany them on the long, leisurely journey across the channel.

'How do you feel?' Her heart gave a strange little flutter as he closed the door and sat down on the bed, his dark eyes studying her intently.

'Much better.' She was disconcerted by how tremulous her voice sounded, but strangely enough she did feel all right.

Her pale complexion, though, emphasised the dark smudges under her eyes which didn't escape Colt's notice, and solicitously he was asking, 'Can you cope?'

Raine sipped the hot coffee, inhaling its fresh aroma, knowing he was referring to the day ahead. Earlier, she had feared that she wouldn't be able to, but she had been assigned this job because the firm had considered her the most qualified person to do it, and she wasn't going to let them down.

'Yes,' she answered resolutely, and noticed the hint of a smile which flitted around his mouth. Then, for a moment, his gaze flicked down over the pale cream of her shoulders to the flimsy lace of her nightdress covering her generous breasts, and Raine felt a tingling in her veins. She had never seen him like this—so casually dressed—the half-buttoned shirt revealing the dark mat of hair curling against the bronzed velvet of his chest—and she was shocked to find herself wondering what it would feel like to run her fingers over it.

'D-did you mean what you said last night . . . about the islands?' It was all she could think of to say, trying as she was to ignore the peculiar sensations firing through her body, finding that masculinity of his too threatening to her equilibrium, the tug of that dark attraction too strong.

Colt pulled a wry expression, shifting position slightly so that the bed creaked in protest under his weight. 'I wouldn't have said it if I didn't.'

No, she should have known that, she thought, unconsciously licking her lips. He wasn't a man to make idle conversation, or ever say things he didn't mean. Which made his threats to bring her to her knees all the more intimidating.

Rays of sunlight were filtering into the cabin through the low, elongated window, picking out the highlights in the tawny hair. The strong features, though, were turned away from it and in shadow, so that they looked grim and pirate-hard. Like the plunderers she had envisaged last night, ravaging their virgin lands, she couldn't help thinking, and then told herself firmly that she was having far too many delusions about the man.

'When I lived in England, London stifled me,' he was saying heavily, as if he didn't even care for the memory of it. 'My ambition was to make money to get out of it. Not, as Jocelyn suggested, the other way around. I didn't want to be too far away from England, but I wanted somewhere away from the rat-race. Consequently . . .' his mouth compressed from some inner satisfaction '. . . when I came here twelve years ago, it was like a realisation of all my dreams.' He looked so inwardly pleased—like a schoolboy who had found a long-lost treasure and was keeping it very much to himself—that Raine couldn't absorb enough of him. When the boat suddenly rolled, she would have lost the cup from her saucer if Colt hadn't had the razor-sharp reflex action to steady it. 'I conduct a lot of business in London,' he continued, 'but I could never go back.' And, with a half-amused, half-reprehending twist to his lips, he was adding, 'And I believe I've told you that before.'

Which proved what a good memory he had, she thought, because he had—six years ago. It was during a visit to his house. She had been telling him how, when her father used to take her to England, they'd always had to visit an uncle in London, and that she'd hated every minute of it. She remembered realising an odd pleasure in discovering that he felt the same way as she did towards city life. But at least, then, she'd had his respect . . .

'Yes, you did,' she murmured quietly, turning to him, and winced at the pain which stabbed through her shoulder blade.

'Headache still troubling you?'

Of course, that shrewd eye of his wouldn't miss a thing.

'It's just a bit of a stiff neck.' She shrugged it off, not wanting to make a fuss. The movement made her wince again, though she hid the discomfort well this time. 'It's a legacy of migraine, sometimes.'

'Then let's see if we can do something about it, shall we?'

To her utter discomfiture, he was taking her cup and saucer, ignoring her sudden protests that the pain wasn't really that bad as he placed the crockery down on the small teak cabinet with a soft clink.

When he touched her, her breath seemed to catch in her lungs, the lightest brush of his hand against her shoulder as he pushed back her hair, making her heart beat thunderously. But, when his fingers found the point of pain in her neck, she sucked in her breath sharply and he said quietly, but firmly, 'Turn over.'

She did as he instructed, her whole body tensing as he slipped the thin straps off her shoulders, replacing them with the cool touch of his hands, her small gasp of awareness stifled by the pillow as she prayed hard that he wouldn't notice how fast her heart was beating.

He knew what he was doing, though, his fingers massaging the tight knot of muscles with remarkable skill, so that after a while she began to relax, and gave a small groan of appreciation.

'Better?' The deep velvet of his voice was as soothing as the clever manipulation of his hands, and Raine responded with a long, satisfied sigh. She didn't want to talk. She was being enveloped by a lethargy as pleasurable as it was warm, feeling her tensions easing under the skilled technique of those hands. The gentle rocking of the boat relaxed her, too, so that she wasn't even aware of another tension building deep inside of her, or that her breathing had grown quick and shallow. She was lost in the warm ecstasy of that gentle pressure on her body—on the sensitive flesh of her back and shoulders, spreading outwards and downwards to her waist and the gentle curve of her hips—abandoning herself to it so completely that, by the time she realised what he was doing to her, it was already beyond her control.

When he turned her round, her eyes were slumbrous with desire, and her tousled hair lay like dark fire against the crisp whiteness of the pillow. She gazed up at him, seeing the colour which washed over the tan of his hard features, the latent passion behind that cool mask that she had somehow dangerously aroused.

'Colt . . .' It was a plea for restraint, but its meaning was lost in the husky emotion of her desire. Her lips were parting in unwitting invitation to his, and he bent his head, claiming her mouth with a possession that brought every cell of her being to tingling life in response. She was aching for him, welcoming the weight of him against her softness, the scent and feel of him—the whole whipcord strength of his body.

She gave a small groan as his kiss changed to a slow, languorous exploration of her mouth, his tongue probing the inner sweetness of her lips, the hidden recesses and sensitive areas, coaxing her to give with a persuasion that stripped her of all resistance. She was out of her depth with him, but she didn't care, only aware that she wanted this, burned with a fever for the ecstasy of this man's attentions.

His lips were marking a trail of burning kisses down to the small, throbbing hollow of her throat, and she groaned his name, shuddering with desire.

Her nightdress was being eased over her breasts. She felt their eager response as she anticipated the mind-blowing promise of his touch, gasping as it became reality, sensations rocketing through her that made her languid with need. She had always imagined her breasts were too full, but they seemed made for his hands, their creamy softness, pliant and responsive, milky-white against the hard tan of his own skin.

When she moaned softly, he lifted his head to look at her.

She was lying like an abandoned nymph, one arm flung outwards, the dark pink aureoles of her breasts tumid with arousal. There was a flush high on her cheekbones, her lips were parted, and her eyes were half closed against her desire, and the shaft of light from the now dazzling sun.

'You're very beautiful.' It was a deep, throaty admission, as if it were an effort for him to speak, his eyes dark with the intensity of his own desire, restrained passion stretching the skin tight across his cheekbones. 'My beautiful, abandoned girl.'

Her smile was a response to his, the dark fervour of his gaze capturing hers, holding her in thrall, and unconsciously she lifted a hand to the hard structure of his cheek, drawing it down the firm sweep of his clean-shaven jaw, her breathing ragged as she explored the damp heat of his throat and shoulder, and then, more boldly, the crispness of hair and hard muscle beneath his shirt. He gave a harsh groan, catching her wrist, and then dipped his head to claim one burgeoning breast with his mouth.

Sensation upon sensation shuddered through her, a need so intense that it was like a stabbing in her loins as he tugged on the round, tumescent peak with a gentle action of his teeth, tormenting her mindless with his tongue.

Tremblingly, her lids fluttered apart, a small murmur of pleasure escaping her at the sight of his dark tawny head against the creamy swell of her breast. She tried to clasp him to her, but the straps of her nightdress were impeding her efforts and, as if reading her intentions, Colt halted his sweet torment of her body to tug the flimsy garment down until she was naked save for the bunch of crumpled silk which lay across her loins.

'Oh, God, you drive me mad!'

He was lying full length across her now, and somehow her trembling fingers had freed his shirt from his waistband, delighting in the feel of that coarse hair beneath. She heard him catch his breath as her hands slid around him to gently stroke the strong, flexing muscles of his back.

He was moving, pressing kisses against every inch of creamy flesh exposed to him, taking her on a sensual voyage that threatened to send her delirious. But, as his lips moved intimately down across the flat plane of her stomach, she suddenly tensed, for some reason thinking of the woman he'd loved and married. Brutally, the intrusive thought tugged her mind back on a cold, rationalising course.

Didn't he just want to hurt her? To make her pay for what he thought she'd done? And foolishly, by succumbing to his kisses, she was giving him licence to do just that!

She sucked in a breath and, reaching down, caught the strong hair at the nape of his neck, her fingers as tremulous as her breathless, 'No!'

He stopped kissing her immediately, although he didn't move, except to drop his head against the soft warmth of her abdomen with a sharp breath, as though he were having a job getting himself back under control. His hair, falling forward, brushed her skin—a sensual stimulus even without intent— and, despite all logic, a shock of fresh desire tingled through her, so highly charged that she gave a small gasp, and brought her arms up to clasp them tightly across her breasts, almost as a shield against it, against him.

'Why did you stop me?' He was sitting up, looking down at her so hard that she shivered at the familiar hatred which was back more chillingly than ever in his eyes, though his face was still flushed with passion. 'Were you as keen to stop Tim, or did you allow him the luxury of that lovely body before he went half out of his mind when you finally changed yours?'

'No!' She screamed the word at him, but he wasn't listening; contempt and perhaps pain, too, she reasoned, were contorting his mouth into hard, ugly lines.

'You like changing your mind, don't you, Raine?' Roughly,

he pulled her arms away from her breasts, pinning them on either side of her body and staring down at her, humiliating her with his hot gaze.

Oh, God! Why hadn't she remembered how much he hated her, she thought wildly, before she'd let him ensnare her with the sweet torment of his lovemaking?

'Let me go, Colt.' Although her voice shook, she did manage to say it with some degree of dignity, which was a mistake, she realised, when she saw how his eyes narrowed.

'No,' he said coldly, and with such menacing intent that a little dart of fear quivered through her. What was he intending to do? Fear dampened her skin and she bit down on her lip, closing her eyes against the icy chill of his—the self-loathing and that hard, fierce glint which told her, unmistakably, that he still wanted her. 'You unfeeling little . . .' His grip on her arms tightened, hurting the soft flesh. 'Why did you do it to him?' he grated, one hard jerk shaking her into opening her eyes to him. 'Why?'

Those tough, implacable features frightened her so much that she was twisting to get away from him. She gave a small cry as, suddenly, he straddled her making escape impossible. His vehement '*Why?*' and his prisoning hold gave rein to panic and, uncontrollably, it seemed, the words which were screaming through her brain.

*Because I came home that day and found my fiancé in bed with your wife!*

# CHAPTER FIVE

SHE hadn't said them. And she couldn't. Even when Colt was still pinning her to the bed—his anger hard and tangible—some spark of propriety remained to prevent Raine from disclosing the truth. What he would have done to Tim had she told him—and had he believed her—she dreaded to think. Not that it was her fiancé's pleas for silence that had stopped her doing so six years ago, because at the time she had been so cruelly hurt, she couldn't have cared what Colt did to him.

Her mind in a whirl of chaos, fleetingly she remembered that day—how Tim had been home, supposedly decorating his flat for when they were married, and she, having been given the afternoon off, had called round unexpectedly, wanting to surprise him. Well, it had been a surprise, all right! But for her! She'd let herself into what seemed at first, an empty flat, until she'd glanced through that half-open door and seen them—Tim and his sister-in-law, their naked limbs entwined on the bed in the full, shattering act of betrayal. It had been Stephanie who had seen her, standing there pale and open-mouthed, Stephanie who'd let out a small cry that had made Tim glance over his shoulder, all passion dissolving on a dumbfounded, 'Oh, hell!' Shaken out of her immobilised torture, Raine had fled from the flat—refused to see him again. She'd been too numb, when she'd heard about the accident, to contest the brutal things people were saying about her, though a strict moral code of conduct had prevented her from telling anyone—even her parents—the whole truth, least of all, Colt. And then, of course, when Stephanie had died, it was totally out of the question.

Looking up at those daunting features, hers set in lines that refused to be intimidated, she murmured stoically, 'Why don't you try asking your dear brother again, Colt?'

His eyes darkened, his grip on her arms easing a little. Even so, there was a grim line to the commanding mouth as he stared down into her rebellious face, ignoring her challenge, to deliver with inexorable coolness, 'And what makes you think *I'm* agreeing to let you change your mind?'

Alarm signals rang through her as she realised what he meant, and nervously she cast her tongue over suddenly dry lips. 'You mean . . . you'd rape me?' Was that her voice? So tremulous, so weak?

His smile added no warmth to the stormy eyes. 'Oh, come on, Raine . . .' His hands slid to her shoulders, moving insolently, yet with such sensual proficiency to the outer curve of her breasts that her breath caught painfully in her lungs. 'It wouldn't be rape, would it?'

She pressed her lids tight against the mocking awareness in those handsome features, against the hands which were suddenly adding weight to his words by closing over each soft mound, proving his point as the dark nubs hardened instantly beneath his palms, and she had to grit her teeth to prevent a small, pleasurable sob escaping her.

No, it wouldn't be, she thought, beneath a wave of self-condemnation. He could drive her mindless for him, even though he hated her. God, did she have *no* self-respect . . .

'For goodness' sake! Cover yourself up.' It was a ragged command as he swung away from her, and quickly she grabbed her nightdress, sitting up to clutch it to her.

With her hair falling over one naked shoulder, her face flushed, her eyes luminous with frustration and anger, she threw at him, 'What's wrong, Colt? Does the fun go out of it if you can't have a woman against her will?' And realised how inane that remark was when he swung back to her, bending low, with his arms on the bed, his condemnation so palpable that she could feel it flaying her.

'Don't push me, Raine.' His voice was a low warning, and instinctively she shrank back from the white heat of hatred in his eyes. 'If I chose to rape you, I can promise you you wouldn't like it, so just thank your lucky stars you haven't yet dragged me quite that low.'

And he went out, the cabin door closing behind him with a surprisingly soft click.

The sun was now fully risen. Through the window, the water sparkled silver, blinding in its brilliance, each wave rippling its promise of a perfect day, but Raine couldn't have felt less like enjoying it. She was burning with shame. The way she had let herself behave with Colt had been reckless and totally foolish, and, from his scathing tone before he had left her, had only served to reduce his opinion of her still further. So much for complaining about a stiff neck! But his strength had seemed to emphasise her comparative frailty this morning —heightening her susceptibility to him—and she could only console herself with the thought that, if she hadn't been feeling so vulnerable, he would hardly have been able to have evoked such a response from her. She had to keep telling herself that, otherwise she didn't know how she would get through the day, having to face him again.

Despite her preliminary worries, however, it wasn't so bad. During the buffet breakfast and the ensuing conference, Colt treated her with impeccable courtesy in front of the others. He could switch off against personal involvements while he was working, she realised rather enviously, making him a force to be reckoned with where his business associates were concerned. Positive, forceful, and yet still retaining a sense of humour that earned him the respect even of the older men on board, he oozed a confidence that brought him results, helping him secure a very important deal on *his* terms, that air of leadership and that razor-sharp intellect making the awe-struck Andrew Day beside him pale into insignificance.

Throughout the day, between taking notes and trying to ignore the younger man's rather flirtatious remarks to her—and particularly his sister's blatant interest in Colt—Raine wondered, amazed, how Stephanie Falloner had wound up in Tim's bed, when she had had a husband like Colt. True, she had thought herself enough in love with Tim to want to marry him, but she had been young— too young, she realised wryly, not to be blinded by his rather obvious charm. And it was only now, in full womanhood, that she realised the depth of Colt's character compared with the shallowness of his half-brother's. So what had Stephanie seen in Tim, she reasoned, puzzlingly, when the man she had married could enrapture a woman the way he had enraptured her, Raine?

'Look, the Needles!' Andrew's sudden observation dragged her fevered thoughts from the man sitting opposite her to the group of chalk rocks on the yacht's starboard side, and after that it wasn't long before they were mooring in Lymington's marina on the mainland's south coast.

The Days and their colleagues were returning to their London office and, on dry land again, Raine noticed the way Jocelyn reached up to kiss Colt fully on the mouth as her taxi arrived—standing on tiptoe, one slender hand resting lightly on his dark sleeve. Against a backdrop of boats' masts and sparkling water, and the pale blue of the late afternoon sun, they looked so right together that Raine turned away from them, annoyed that she was experiencing an absurd pang of resentment.

Why should *she* care? she asked herself in the car Colt had hired to take them to the airport. He hardly meant anything to her, after all. And she was glad that the yacht was being taken into Southampton for maintenance and that they were flying back, since that would mean that she wouldn't have to suffer much more than a couple of hours alone with him, she thought, relieved, until she discovered he had plans of his own.

He was pulling off the main road, taking a suspiciously rural-looking turning, and Raine darted him a questioning glance. 'Where are we going?'

His expression was unreadable, the dappled sunlight filtering through the trees on his side of the car, chasing shadows across his face. 'There's someone I want to visit while I'm here.'

Raine eyed him curiously, but he wasn't offering any further explanation, and she gave a small, indiscernible shrug. 'What about our flight?' According to Jack Hardwicke, it had been booked for six, and that was not much more than an hour away.

'I've arranged a later one.' And that, Raine realised, was the end of the subject.

They were in Hampshire's New Forest, the countryside opening up and spreading around them—extensively moorlike in appearance—the brackens, heathers and groundsel predominantly green now, but which later in the year would emblazon the Forest with ambers, purples and golds.

'It's a beautiful part of the country.'

Her quiet observation coaxed a sidelong glance from Colt. 'I think my stepmother would agree with you,' he drawled, putting gentle pressure on the brake to lessen the judder as they crossed a cattle-grid. 'She sold everything in London and chose to come and live here when my father died.'

Raine drew in a breath. It was the first time he had given her a glimpse into his personal background. In fact, she was surprised to realise how little she knew about him. She wanted to know more, and she was eager not to let this opportunity slide.

'And that would have made you about . . . eighteen?'

There was questioning surprise in the look he gave her, an applaud in the way he breathed, 'Good girl.' Clearly, he was impressed.

Actually, it hadn't taken much working out. Raine remembered Tim saying he'd lost the father he'd shared with Colt when he was ten, and Tim *was* eight years younger than his brother. But that she had managed to keep the fact in her memory was obviously beyond Colt's estimation of her, because his comment hadn't been without a tinge of sarcasm, either. She despaired of his continual need to verbally flay her.

'What about your mother?' she queried tentatively, running a hand over the smoothness of her skirt, deciding not to let his cynicism get to her. 'Your real mother, I mean.'

He shrugged, steering the car carefully around a free-roaming bay pony and her foal, giving the animals a wide berth. 'I don't remember her,' he said, somewhat dispassionately. 'She died just after I was born.'

'And your father married again . . . when?'

Her eyes were large green pools of curiosity as they met Colt's, and she saw his mouth pull down one side. 'Not until I was seven.'

A long time, Raine thought, contemplatively. But he seemed more approachable now than she had known him since she had come back, and so she pressed on, 'You must have been close to him, then.'

He didn't answer for a moment, changing gear to overtake a crawling farm vehicle, before saying, 'No, not particularly. My father worked away from home a lot, and my early days consisted of a long line of nannies and housekeepers, so I didn't see much of him. He also believed that boarding school was the best thing for a kid, so consquently I never really got to know him that well.' Had she imagined that hint of regret in his voice? 'Perhaps he thought he was right,' she heard Colt continuing, 'but personally I feel that a child should be with its parents . . . for the first and most important years of its development, at least.'

Raine couldn't agree more, but she didn't voice her opinion, sensing that she would be treading on quicksand if she did. He couldn't always have his own son with him, and he blamed her for that. Nevertheless, silently she sympathised, only half able to imagine the loneliness Colt must have suffered as a child. Perhaps that was why he was so self-sufficient, so independent —now.

She looked out of the window; saw the small herds of Forest ponies grazing—unaware of them—on the grassy verge, and she turned back to Colt, her hair shining like dark fire as it caught the sunlight.

'What about your stepmother? Did you get on well with her?' she asked. Then wished she hadn't when he drew up abruptly at a junction and stared at her hard.

'What is this, Raine? An interrogation?' he queried icily, his brows drawing together. And the squeal of tyres as he pulled away again reflected his sudden impatience with her.

So she was all right to share a bed with, but not his private life, she thought woundedly, when he plunged them both into silence by answering her. After that, she gazed numbly out of the windscreen at the village they were passing through, at the little cottages, a church, a red-brick farmhouse, until suddenly, anxiously, she was saying, 'Colt . . . we aren't going to your stepmother's now?' It had only just occurred to her that they might well be, and a shiver ran through her. She had never met her ex-fiancé's mother. Couldn't even remember Tim ever visiting the woman himself during the time she had known him, and, although it had been arranged for Raine to meet her a week before the wedding, obviously the meeting had never taken place. But surely the woman would remember her name—the girl who had supposedly brought so much suffering to her sons? So what sort of reception would she be likely to get if Colt turned up with her now?

'Relax,' he drawled, obviously aware of her misgivings, and the tension in her. 'For some strange reason, she always refused to condemn you wholeheartedly, so you'll probably find her more tolerant towards you than you deserve.'

Raine's mouth tightened as she struggled to hold back some

biting retort. What was the point? she thought exasperatedly, and turned away from him, wishing she could be unprincipled enough to fling the truth at him. Hurt him with it. Enjoy seeing that cool mask slip as he learned about his precious little wife's unfaithfulness with his brother. But she couldn't, even for her own sake. Which meant that she would just have to keep suffering the cruel lash of his tongue, she thought unhappily, her sudden cogitation over what he had said about his stepmother quickly replaced by a sick feeling in her stomach as he pulled up outside a rambling, thatched cottage.

The garden was beautiful, miniature rose-bushes—not yet in flower—growing beside perennials and annuals which were reflecting the painstaking care of a loving gardener in the pinks and golds and amethysts which trimmed the path to the front door. But there was no response to Colt's knock, and Raine breathed a sigh of relief. Prematurely, she realised, when he uttered, 'Around the back.'

Obviously he knew his stepmother's habits well, because he was right, Raine discovered, noticing the two people bending over a pond in the larger, rear garden. It was the smaller of them who spotted their visitors first.

'Daddy!'

The boy was scampering towards them, and Raine's throat constricted as she heard Colt's deep, emotion-filled greeting, saw the way he swept his son up into his arms, one strong hand cradling the child's head—soft and blond against the darker tawny of his own—the other clutching him with a fierce possession that tore at Raine's heart. There was no doubt how much Sean meant to him.

His eyes met hers over the little boy's head, and he must have seen the dark emotion in them because there was a transient question in the hard amber of his, a thin line between his brows. Then the emotionless mask was swiftly replaced and he was stooping to set the boy back on his feet.

'Sean . . . you probably don't remember Miss Welland,

do you?'

The child looked up at her with his little brows drawing together, looking so much like Colt that her heart gave a strange lurch. Apart from the colour of his hair, there was very little of Stephanie in him, and that would probably darken in time, she cogitated—become more like his father's.

'You met her once or twice when you were a toddler,' Colt explained gently to his son.

Raine took the little hand extended to her, Sean's solemn, 'How do you do?' drawing a burst of laughing surprise from her and had her marvelling at the precociousness of the seven-year-old. Clearly, he'd inherited his father's sharp brain, too!

But it was Colt she was more aware of—of those long, brown hands on the boy's shoulders; the way the sun reddened the highlights in his hair so that, when he straightened and looked down at her, holding her prisoner for a few moments with the glittering intensity of his eyes, she felt a flood of warmth gush along her veins, knew that inevitable clutch of desire in her loins.

'Colston!'

The woman's voice broke the silent intimacy between them, leaving Raine mutely berating herself. Such awareness of the man spelt danger, a small, inner voice warned her.

'Mother.' It was a formal greeting on both sides, but there was nothing impersonal about the way Colt's arm slid around the woman's shoulders, or the way his lips brushed against the greying strands at her temple.

Tall and slim, she had a serious face, but a pleasant one, and Raine deduced that there was kindness, and a quiet strength in the matronly features. Even so, she tensed as Colt introduced her to the woman.

Shrewd eyes looked puzzlingly back at Colt, so that he said simply, coolly, 'Yes, the same Raine Welland.' Then, 'We've found ourselves working together.' And that was all. No further explanations, no apologies, which left Raine feeling as awkward as he looked relaxed.

'I hope you won't mind me not shaking hands.' Ruth
Falloner, as her name turned out to be, glanced down at her
own—enmeshed in grubby rubber gloves, one clutching
secateurs—and she grimaced. 'I'm afraid you'll need to call
when it's dark, Raine, to find me anywhere else but in the
garden.'

Which was why it looked so beautiful, Raine thought. This
one—like the one at the front of the house—was a picture with
its neatly trimmed lawn, budding bedding plants and pink
blossoming fruit trees contesting with the gold of a laburnum.
And Raine told her so.

Ruth laughed her thanks, her appreciation matched only by
her tact, Raine decided uneasily, because the woman was
clearly not questioning Colt's motives for bringing her here,
much to Raine's silent gratitude.

'Will you come and see my new fish, Daddy?' Sean was
tugging at his sleeve and was repaid with a smile of such
tender indulgence that Raine knew a twist of envy. Just to have
him smile at her like that!

'He won a goldfish at the school fête this morning,' Ruth
chuckled to them. 'And now he's got it in his mind to start his
own aquarium!'

This brought a burst of amusement from both Raine and
Colt, his deep laughter echoing hers. As he crouched down
beside the pond to look at the small, darting gold arrows the
little boy was pointing out to him, she knew instinctively that,
despite his attitude towards *her,* his discipline and his love for
Sean would be justly balanced so that his son would grow up
as a sensible and caring adult. In fact, the three of them could
have been taken for a family, it struck her suddenly, as she
breathed in the warm sweetness of freshly mown grass.
Because like this, standing beside Colt while he bent over his
son, they might have been any married couple visiting relatives
for the day.

Her thinking startled her and she turned away, ostensibly to admire a pretty, variegated creeper on the wall of the house, while trying to make some sense of her wild imaginings. Was she wishing that Sean was *her* son? That Colt was . . . her *husband?*

The thought was absurd and she shook it away, trying to give all her attention to Ruth, who was explaining about the creeper—promising to let her have a cutting when the season was right—and Raine stared abstractedly at the small, pointed leaves, telling herself that she had merely become ensnared by a powerful sexuality.

Ridiculously, her body craved Colt's with an insane hunger that had nothing to do with logic, that ignored the fact of his blatant contempt for her and her own instincts of self-preservation, which warned her that she was heading for trouble. She wanted to go to bed with him, to abandon herself to his lovemaking and the mindless ecstasy of his possession. But it was only a sexual thing, and so against her moral principles that her brain was merely attempting to justify her feelings by making her think there was more to it than that, when there wasn't. Still, lust or whatever, it was such a driving and overpowering emotion that even now she coud feel the ache of unsated desire so strong in her that she couldn't meet the lucidity of his eyes as he joined her with Sean, afraid that he would recognise the betraying turmoil in hers.

They had tea on the patio, a leisurely meal of sandwiches and light cakes, and, while Colt discussed general family matters with his stepmother, Raine chatted freely to the little boy. He surprised her occasionally with little scraps of knowledge she would have thought him too young to have acquired, and guessed that it was through Colt's influence, his unyielding resolve to take an interest in, and bring up, his own son. She glanced up with admiration in her eyes, and before she could conceal it he had looked across at her, caught her expression. The subtlest acknowledgement, in the lifting of an eyebrow, caused her to blush. But for the moment, at least, there was no animosity between them.

The sun was dipping low behind the trees, the light making the new season's leaves appear a rich gold, and from another garden came the distant whine of a lawn-mower.

'Sean, why don't you take Daddy to see the seedlings we've been planting out in the greenhouse?' Ruth suggested, pushing back her chair to clear away the dishes.

Sean didn't need to be told twice. Jumping up, he was scampering away with Colt in his wake, shrieking happily as his father caught him and swept him high into the air.

Raine's face softened as she watched them, and she recognised another tug of envy at the affection Colt showed towards the boy.

'I'll give you a hand,' she offered, helping Ruth, grateful for the chance to get away from Colt for a while. He disturbed her far too much. And besides, she wanted to talk to Ruth alone because, at the very least, she felt she owed the woman some sort of apology for turning up on her doorstep like this.

Fortunately, Ruth allowed herself to be convinced that Raine would rather be in the kitchen than following the other two, and together they carried the dishes inside.

'Well?' the woman began without any preamble when they were in the large, flagstoned kitchen, her serious features breaking into a smile when she saw the question in Raine's. 'Oh, yes,' Ruth breathed, sagely, 'I know there's something on your mind. I also know that Colston won't give any explanations if he doesn't consider them necessary, and that's been making you feel uncomfortable ever since you arrived, hasn't it?'

Raine stared down into the white, foamy water filling the sink, thinking how shrewd Ruth Falloner was. As shrewd as Colt, though there were no blood-ties between them. She shrugged, her brow furrowing. 'It's just that I didn't know Colt intended bringing me here,' she admitted awkwardly.

'It's unfortunate enough that we've been thrown together in the office. But coming here . . .' The apology was there in her voice as she began washing up. 'It must have been rather a shock for you, too.'

The woman's smile was dismissive. 'I've been around too long to be shocked by much these days, dear,' she said calmly, drying one of the pretty, rose-patterned plates. 'What happened between you and my son wasn't a matter for anyone else—only the two of you. And if Colston chooses to bring you here, then that's his affair, not mine.'

Raine offered a wan smile, warming to Colt's stepmother. So he'd been right when he had said Ruth hadn't prejudged her, though Raine still wondered why.

'About Tim . . . there were reasons,' she explained, meeting his mother's gaze with a guileless honesty, desperately wanting her to know. Yet she couldn't say any more than that, and was surprised to feel a reassuring pat on her arm.

'He never once brought you to see me, did he?' Ruth sighed, pushing back an offending grey hair. 'In fact, he comes less than ever these days.' Raine detected a sadness in the older woman's voice. 'Colston, on the other hand, comes regularly,' she was continuing, 'regardless of whether Sean's with me or not. Whenever he's in England, he'll always try to fit in a visit before he flies back.'

There was an unmistakable pride in the way Ruth told her that, and Raine felt a tug of deepening respect for Colt. Not that it was a new emotion to her. That adolescent awe of him had been respect of a sort, and Colt was the type of man who would naturally command it wherever he went, without even being conscious of it. But what Ruth had said only confirmed what she already knew—that family ties were important to him. If they weren't, then he wouldn't have hated *her* quite so much, she reminded herself chillingly.

'You're very fond of him, aren't you?'

Raine's soft observation had the effect of lighting up Ruth's strong features. 'As if he was my own flesh and blood. He's been more like a son to me than my own, yet we didn't really get to know each other until my husband died.' Surprised by her remark, Raine watched her hanging cups from little pegs on the oak dresser which filled nearly one wall, noting how well cared for her nimble figure was beneath the quality plaid skirt and cotton blouse. 'When I married his father,' Ruth was explaining, turning back to her, 'Colston was already at boarding-school, you see.' She shrugged. 'It was a pity, but father and son were too alike and didn't hit it off.' Remembering made Ruth's mouth twist wryly. 'Both dominating. Both stubborn. And both with unshakeable wills of their own.' She smiled. 'Infuriating to live with, Raine, but tolerable when it goes hand in hand with consideration, loyalty and a strong sense of responsibility, and it did. Does,' she corrected. 'Especially with Colston.'

Washing a cup, Raine caught the fragrance of a wistaria which was trained along the wall above the open window, its scent heady and evocative. She wondered what Colt would say if he knew his stepmother was discussing him with her like this, and dreaded to imagine. 'Was his father strict with him?' she found herself asking.

'Very.' Ruth Falloner's reply was somewhat disapproving, Raine thought. Then understood when the woman went on, 'It didn't do him any harm, but even so, I used to think he'd got an unfair crack of the whip, so to speak, at times . . . being sent away so young . . . being left to his own devices. And Henry was so much more lenient with Timothy. If he hadn't been, I doubt if there would have been so much sibling rivalry between them.'

Raine turned to the woman, red curls tumbling across her shoulder. 'You mean . . . Colt was jealous of Tim?' she asked, surprised. She found that hard to believe.

'Oddly enough, it was the other way around,' she was even more astonished to hear Ruth say. 'Timothy always wanted what Colston had. To do everything he did,' she elucidated, picking up the discarded petals of a large, pink Busy Lizzie which stood proudly on the kitchen windowsill, 'and, of course, after their father died, things were difficult for me. It was only through Colston financing his brother's education that Timothy managed to go on to college, and I'm sure you know how his brother gave him his first job, took him with him when he moved the company to Jersey, even paid for his flat.' This last was new to Raine, although she'd known the rest about Tim's beginnings from Tim himself.

'He's still working for Colston . . . in the original company,' Ruth enlightened her, tossing the petals into the bin, and Raine detected an oddly exasperated note to her voice. 'I expect he's told you.'

He hadn't, and Raine hadn't wanted to ask—or anything else about her ex-fiancé. But she remembered how often he'd tried to emulate his brother—attain that elegance, that air of command—and without the same success. But that he'd always wanted what Colt had . . . Inwardly, Raine flinched. Little did Ruth know that that had included Colt's wife, as well!

Through the window, she could see his tall figure in the greenhouse at the far end of the lawn, bending interestedly to something the little boy was holding, and she swallowed, more affected by Colt's love for his son than she wanted to be. 'I wish he could accept that there were two sides to the story . . . with Tim and me,' she murmured wistfully to Ruth, who was putting cutlery in a drawer. 'But he still blames me for the accident.'

'Still?' Coming away from the dresser, Ruth looked surprised. 'I was hoping he'd let bygones be bygones,' she sighed, drying the last plate, 'but I suppose, emotionally, he was hurt as much as anyone was by it. And it isn't helping much at the moment, seeing what it's done to Timothy.'

Raine sent her a questioning look, sensing that she had been about to say something else—sensing also that Ruth wasn't just talking about her son's physical disability.

'And of course . . . he lost Stephanie.'

For some reason, Ruth's remark gave rise to a shiver of some indefinable emotion in Raine, and this time she couldn't look at the older woman, pulling the plug from the sink and watching the water swirl slowly away. As her pride would if she were foolish enough to get involved with him, she couldn't help thinking fatalistically.

'I think we'd better get back to the boys before they come looking for us, don't you?' Ruth's smile was warm and, agreeing, Raine returned it, first excusing herself to go to the bathroom.

Freshening up, she though how pleasant her hostess was. When Colt had brought her here, she had hoped for perhaps tolerance from Tim's mother, but definitely not warmth—friendship, even! It just proved what a kind and fair person she was, Raine decided—unable to be swayed by her emotions as Colt was. But then, as Ruth had so correctly pointed out to her, he had lost the most.

Coming back downstairs, she made to join the others, but paused in the hall, hearing a knock at the front door. When Colt had knocked earlier, Ruth hadn't heard him in the garden, she remembered, and so it was probably unlikely that she would have heard whoever was there now. She deliberated over whether to answer it herself, and decided she would, tripping lightly down the passageway and opening the door, only to receive the second worst shock of her life.

# CHAPTER SIX

OPEN-MOUTHED, Raine was staring up into a pair of familiar blue eyes, the once splendid features hardened by the ugly scar across one cheek. Hair fairer than Colt's crowned an equally fair complexion, which at that moment seemed to have been drained of all colour.

'What the hell are you doing here?' The smooth voice that had once had the power to make her legs go weak was now laced with a burning distaste and, recovering from her initial shock, somehow Raine managed to find her tongue.

'Tim, I . . .' She didn't know what to say, wondered what he was doing there. She was only vaguely aware of Sean running up behind her, of his stopping dead, almost as if he had been chastened, when he recognised his uncle and, her mind in a turmoil, she was uttering, 'Colt brought me.'

'*Mother?*' It was a hard accusation rather than a greeting, his face contorting as his gaze swept past Raine and the little boy. With a mixture of bewilderment and chilling pity, she watched Tim limp clumsily through the doorway, aided by a stick, only aware then that the other two were behind her.

Ruth looked pale, she thought dazedly. As pale as her son. And only Colt, tall and forbidding beside her, seemed apparently unperturbed by this untimely appearance of his half-brother—his expression impassive, inscrutable. And it occurred to Raine then why he would be. Tim's visits to his mother were too few for this to be some frightful coincidence, and with her eyes burning through Colt she tore past him, ignoring the way he called after her, and fleeing into the garden, fighting back tears of wounded anger and frustration.

How could he? Did he hate her so much that he could expose her to the horrors of what her refusing to marry Tim had caused? Force her to face them? Accept them as *her* doing?

'Raine!' Colt was behind her, turning her to face him, but she managed to twist away from him, her eyes venomous.

'You indescribable bastard!' Every cell in her body throbbed hatred towards him, the tears streaming down her face, not for Timothy, but because of Colt's unbelievable cruelty. 'You arranged it! You brought me here . . . got Tim to come here just so you coud force me to see him like that . . . you . . . you . . .' Her fingers were trying to make clawing contact with his face, but he caught them in his own, forcing her hands down until they were behind her back, holding her sobbing and protesting against him.

'Raine! For God's sake, get a grip on yourself!' He shook her gently. 'Do you really think I had something to do with that?' He jerked his head roughly towards the house. 'Admittedly, I want to see you answer for what you did, but only to me.' His voice was husky with some raw emotion that made her look up at him enquiringly, some nameless emotion in her crying out to those hard, implacable features in silent appeal for his understanding, his tenderness, his respect. And, as if her feelings had conveyed themselves to him, his hands slid gently along the silky sleeves of her suit to her shoulders, their warmth penetrating the thin jacket, sending a host of startling sensations through her.

'It's pure coincidence,' she heard him say stoically above the light rustle of sycamore leaves behind them. 'But regardless of how it probes that pretty conscience of yours, you're going to have to——'

'Very touching.' Timothy's derisive words cut across Colt's, making them both turn sharply. Standing so close to Colt, Raine realised how it must look. 'And it's no coincidence, brother, dear.' He limped across the patio, his build and height a mere shadow of Colt's, his stick making a dull tap on the paving stones. 'I rang your office, but they said you were in England, so I flew over. I guessed you wouldn't miss a chance to play the dutiful son.' There was raw antagonism—a tangible resentment—in Timothy towards his brother that Raine hadn't seen in him six years ago, and his eyes narrowed as he looked at her and Colt, now standing apart. 'Well, it seems I've got the answer to what I wanted to know.' His voice was thick with contempt. 'Now I'm beginning to understand why you had the bloody nerve to authorise a withdrawal of my expense account—threaten my job.'

'You've been gambling too much,' was Colt's cool, succinct reply.

'And what else is there for me to do, for Christ's sake?' The bitterness in the younger man's voice pierced through Raine. Yes, he had changed from the charming and rather cocksure young man she'd met first at a party and fallen instantly in love with, she realised unhappily, and guessed that it was this resentment and bitterness to which Ruth had alluded earlier. Despite how he'd hurt her though, Raine felt another tug of pity for him. She heard Sean's puzzled call to his father from the doorway, then Ruth ushering him diplomatically back inside.

'It's all right for you,' Timothy was snarling up at his half-brother, 'with your own personal empire, your fancy car and your money. But women don't exactly fall into my lap these days.' He laughed, an ugly sound that made Raine shudder. 'So how does it feel playing around with what used to be *my* girl?'

'Tim!'

Clearly, the results of the accident had embittered him beyond belief. There was a palpable hostility between the two men—engendered by Tim, Raine felt—that could have been cut with a knife.

'Well, what's she been telling you?' Ignoring Raine's sharp reprimand, he looked suspiciously at Colt, his mouth contorting unpleasantly, and it suddenly occurred to Raine that he obviously suspected her of telling his brother about Stephanie and himself. And, with a derogatory look at her, he went on, 'Has she told you how good it was between us, Colt? Quite a wildcat in bed, isn't she?'

'Timothy!' It came out simultaneously with some whispered admonition from Colt, so she didn't catch what he said, but she was livid with Tim. 'I'm just working for Colt . . . nothing more,' she threw at him poignantly, despising her ex-fiancé for debasing her even further in his brother's eyes. She had never been to bed with Tim, never once let him make love to her during that brief engagement, wanting—naïve as she had been!—to keep herself for him until after they were married, despite his continual attempts to try and change her mind. Now, when she thought about it, she wanted to laugh at the artless creature she had been.

She heard the splash of a fish in the ornamental pond, followed by the younger man's cruel laughter. 'Oh, come on, sweetheart. What I saw just now went beyond the bounds of official duty. But are you sure he can satisfy you? Sure he's what you want?' His knuckles showed white where they gripped the top of the walking stick, but a hateful sneer was curling his lower lip. 'A man who couldn't even hang on to his own wife?'

'What are you driving at, Tim?' Colt's harsh retort seemed to slice the air, and a small murmur of protest left Raine's lips. From this rancour in Timothy, she sensed only a desire to hurt his brother. To make him pay for . . . for what? Having his health and strength? Things the accident *he'd* caused had robbed him of? And if he thought that she'd already told Colt . . .

'Tim, don't,' she pleaded, trying to prevent an ugly scene between the two brothers, and Colt from suffering more than he had already. Which was odd, she thought ironically, when he still wanted so much to hurt her . . .

She saw Timothy's face whiten. 'You mean, you haven't told him?'

There was incredulity in his voice as it tailed off, but Colt's demand cut across the silence like a whiplash. 'Haven't told me what?' He took a step towards his brother and, unwittingly, Raine caught at his arm, fearing what a revelation might lead to.

'It's nothing, Colt . . .'

'Nothing?' Timothy's tone was sarcastic, and his free hand raked agitatedly through his hair. 'Your loyalty's commendable, Raine, but you'd have told him eventually,' he muttered, and with a grudging look in Colt's direction, 'I'm told his powers of persuasion with women are second to none. Well, it's about time he knew.' And now she realised that he didn't care, that hurting his brother was the only thing that mattered to him. And her desperate, 'Tim!' was futile, as he breathed with a reckless cruelty, 'Why shouldn't he know how you walked in and found Stephanie in bed with me?'

She wasn't sure what happened next, alive only to Colt's fierce growl as he lunged towards Timothy, though she thought she heard Ruth gasp from the doorway. But, almost unaware of it, Raine had flung herself between the two men, her eyes a wide, desperate appeal, her cry a frenzied, 'Colt, no!'

He had stopped dead, his fists clenched at his sides, his teeth clamped hard together, and there was a white line around his mouth from the rigid set of his jaw. A chilling gust came from nowhere, and she shivered, and behind her she heard Timothy's mocking triumph.

'Your concern for me still is touching, darling, but unnecessary. My brother wouldn't stoop to hitting a cripple. It's beyond that supreme integrity of his.'

Dazedly, Raine realised her action could well have looked as though she were protecting Tim, when she didn't know what had made her come between them like that, but she realised

now that he was probably right. It was that immense control of
Colt's that had stopped him from striking his brother, rather
than her reckless and desperate appeal to him; instinctively,
she knew that. And Tim must have reckoned on that
unwavering self-control, otherwise he'd probably never have
been bold enough to spring the truth on Colt like that.
Bewildered, she wondered why he had. Perhaps it had been
the burden of guilt as much as bitterness that had driven him
to say it, in which case, perhaps he'd almost been hoping that
Colt *would* hit him . . .

'My own brother!' Colt's low whisper held abhorrence, but
his anguish was apparent in the tense lines of his mouth and
jaw, in the storm-dark depths of his eyes. Incredibly, Raine felt
his pain; she wondered how she would have coped in his
position—finding out, with one cruel blow, that both a brother
and a spouse had been disloyal, and with each other—and
knew she couldn't possibly imagine the torture of such a
discovery. She wanted to say something, to take away the
tormented look on his face, but couldn't think of anything that
would help.

Close by, she heard Ruth's whispered, 'Colston?'

He looked across at her, a pained query in his eyes. 'Did you
know about this?' he exhaled, with a hard lift of his chest.

Ruth hesitated. 'I suspected something,' she admitted
unhappily. Which was why the woman hadn't condemned
her, it dawned on Raine, some time later.

The mellow warmth of the day had gone. Across the lawn,
the wind made ripples on the pond, and above the trees the
fresh breeze was bringing grey clouds scudding inland from
the sea. Raine shivered again. She felt the strength of Colt's
hand on her upper arm as he put her gently behind him and
stood facing his brother squarely.

'Just thank your lucky stars you're already carrying a stick,'
she heard him snarl, 'or by heaven, I'd have seen to it that
you'd have needed one!'

She had seen him hurting and angry before; outraged even, when he had called on her that day after Stephanie had been killed. But even then she couldn't remember seeing him like this, his pain so palpable she could almost touch it.

'Funny, isn't it, Colt . . . that she preferred me to you?' She couldn't believe that Tim could still want to hurt his brother so much, but he was pressing his luck with Colt's patience, she thought, shuddering, still so dazed by what had happened, it hadn't yet sunk in that Tim's spiteful disclosure had removed all blame from her. 'You know, she wanted to leave you, Colt . . . move in with me.' He laughed. 'Could you have stood that . . . losing your wife to your insignificant little half-brother?'

If he had been stoking up a fire in provoking Colt's anger before, then he was adding kindling fuel to it now, Raine thought, with a small tremor of fear running through her, and was surprised when the broad shoulders merely squared, then relaxed. The muscles of Colt's face had relaxed themselves, too, and he seemed more in command of himself, the inscrutable mask back in place, so that he appeared surprisingly controlled.

'You've been deluded, little brother, if you're flattering yourself that you were the only one.' He took a sharply drawn breath. 'Stephanie had several lovers, and not always in succession, either. The only redeeming factor was that she was remarkably discreet.' Colt's face hardened, and a muscle pulled at the side of his jaw. 'What I didn't know was that she'd be indiscriminate enough to try and seduce a member of my own family . . . and that you could have been such a perfidious little jerk!' His mouth curled disdainfully. 'I can't bear to stay under the same roof with you.'

As he swung away, Raine stood, impaled by his revelation, only half aware that what colour there had been in Tim's cheeks had completely drained out of them. She saw Ruth start towards Colt, but was immobilised herself, her mind in a total whirl over what had been said. She couldn't take it all in, not yet, the fact that, at last, the truth had finally come out. Numbly, she watched Ruth and Colt go inside and made to go after them. Then she flinched, as Tim's fingers suddenly encircled her wrist, stalling her.

'I'm sorry,' he muttered. 'I really am. About what happened with Stephanie, I mean.' He looked contrite, if that were possible, Raine thought. Even with the scar marring otherwise perfect lineaments, he was still a very handsome man. Without Colt's strength of character of course, but attractive, nevertheless. 'He had so much,' Timothy went on, as if that made it all right, and Raine guessed that he wasn't just talking about material assets. 'I didn't think having a bit of fun with his wife would hurt. It was only a lark, anyway, but I only ever really wanted you, yet you . . . you drove me insane with your innocent kisses and your damned virginal principles . . .' His teeth clenched, no doubt from remembering the frustrations he had suffered while they had been going out together, his grip tightening as she tried to pull away. 'Can't you see, it was you who drove me to Stephanie?'

'How dare you say that?' Raine exhaled bitterly, her eyes sparkling with anger, her nostrils flaring from the disgust she felt, the repelling proximity of him. 'You can't blame me any longer for anything that happened then. It's out. Colt knows. Now, if you don't mind, would you please let go of my hand?'

He didn't, jerking her so hard against him that she almost lost her balance, and had to grasp at the sleeve of the light jacket he was wearing to steady herself.

'We could still make a go of it,' she heard him say, unbelievably, as, sickened, she tried to pull away from him. 'You can't possibly entertain the hope that you'll hit it off with Colt.' He grimaced, the wind blowing strands of blond hair across his face. 'As well as being too young for him, you're not his type. But we could be good together. And now that you're older . . . more experienced . . .' He pulled her hand to his lips and, horrified by what he was suggesting, she could only stare at him for a moment, thinking that what Ruth had said about him wanting everything Colt had, must have become an illness with him, because he thought *she* was Colt's. And what else but insanity would lend him the audacity to think she'd even consider going out with him again after the way he'd treated her? she thought acridly, surprised when he suddenly released her. And then she realised why.

Colt had come out of the house, his eyes narrowing as he looked from Raine to his brother, and she couldn't tell whether he had seen that gesture of Tim's, or, if he had, how he had interpreted it. But his tone was icy as he commanded, 'Get your things together. We're leaving.' With no apology, no softening towards her as he turned and went back inside. Shooting a last, cold look at his brother, Raine followed him, feeling more as if she had just been sentenced rather than acquitted.

There was a stony silence between them as Colt drove them to Southampton. It had been arranged that he would take Sean back with him for the weekend, and the little boy, having expended his energies in a burst of lively chatter when he'd first got into the car, was now drowsing in the back. It had started to rain, just odd drops here and there, so that Colt brought the intermittent use of the wiper blades into play, pushing a button for the radio at the same time.

Perhaps he felt he needed something to relieve the strained atmosphere, but some penitent words from him would have been a better start, Raine thought grievously, staring out at the lush, open countryside they were entering again. The music, though, was soothing in its way—a classical piece which she recognised after a moment as Debussy's 'Clair de Lune'. Letting her head drop back against the head-rest, she closed her eyes, allowing the soft, plaintive theme to ease some of her tensions. And she wondered afterwards if Colt had put it on for that purpose, rather than just to break an uneasy silence, because when she opened her eyes again, he shot a glance her way and murmured deeply, 'That's better.' Turning back to the road, he surprised her by saying with a hard sigh, 'Well . . . it seems I was wrong about you.'

That was an understatement! She controlled the sudden rush of hurt anger by taking a deep breath, responding with a simple, though no less censuring, 'Yes.'

He glanced at her again, noticing the piqued set to her lips, the flared, freckle-enhanced nostrils and the hurt emotion in her eyes, and rather impatiently he said, 'What was I suppose to think, Raine? When I trusted my brother and he was cut up enough over you to drink himself silly and go out and crash his car? And you didn't tell me the truth . . . why?' After a moment, he suggested gently, 'Because of what you thought I'd do to Tim?'

Is that what he thought? She looked at him aghast, then back at the windscreen, uttering rather reprovingly, 'No, of course not.'

'Then why?'

It was a hard demand, but when her eyes met his across the small space, she couldn't answer him. But he knew.

There was an incredulous, burning question in his eyes as his concentration on the road lapsed for mere seconds, although there was no fear of any danger—she knew he was too good a driver for that—and when he turned away from her again she heard him curse himself under his breath. 'Good God, Raine, you must enjoy punishment!'

His heavy reproof had her guessing that he wasn't just referring to the kind dished out through detrimental gossip about her in the past, but to his own more recent and particular brand, and warm colour stained her cheeks. The sight of those long, lean hands on the wheel were too vivid a reminder of how intimately she had let him caress her and, burning with shame, she tossed back, 'If you thought I actually liked your threats . . . wanted you to . . .'

'To what?' he challenged when she didn't finish, and there was the barest curve to his mouth as he glanced her way. She couldn't meet his gaze, too aware of him—of how much she had wanted him—and she looked away, feeling Debussy's music like a tangible sensuality between them. Absently watching a pony trot out of their path to the safety of the green verge, she heard Colt say, 'There's no getting away from it, darling. There's an amazing chemistry between us, and whether you want to accept it or not, you responded to me, Raine.' And, with a hard resolve that made her pulse suddenly leap, he added, 'As you'll always respond when I touch you. And if we didn't have Sean with us, cramped though it is in this car, I'd prove it to you.'

She swallowed, casting a stealthy glance at the silent little figure in the back. Seven years of slumbering innocence, and all that protected her from Colt and the traitorous responses of her own body! She couldn't have been more grateful that he was there.

'Such a shame you won't have the chance,' she snapped, to conceal her discomfiture, hoping he wouldn't guess how her heart was suddenly pounding in her breast. 'Otherwise it might have been too demoralising for you, finding yourself wrong twice in the same day.'

He glanced in his rear-view mirror, then back at the road. 'Raine Welland . . . you'll live to rue those words,' he promised softly, switching off the radio because a brass band had struck into a lively march. Raine felt a little frisson of excitement shiver through her. Surely, now that he knew the truth about Tim and Stephanie, and wasn't seeking revenge in her own, unwilling surrender, he wouldn't pursue just a cold-blooded sexual interest in her, would he? Because that was all it was. And in that second her thoughts turned to the woman he had loved enough to marry, the knowledge still amazing her that Stephanie had had affairs with other men as well as Tim, and that, more surprisingly, Colt had known about them.

Surely he must have suffered because of it? Yet he'd hid any personal distress well, she thought, with a deepening admiration for him, although it was ironic to think that, if she'd gone to him and told him the truth six years ago, he'd have been hurt, it was true, but probably he would have believed her then, understood . . .

'Why didn't you divorce her . . . Stephanie, I mean?' The question slipped out before she could stop it, and she looked at him tentatively, but that cool, impassive mask gave nothing away.

'There were reasons,' he answered on one long, shuddering breath. And none better than that he had probably still loved her, Raine thought, self-censuringly, and wondered at the hot little surge of emotion that made her wish she hadn't asked.

'Well . . . will you accept my apologies?'

They had come out of the Forest, and were approaching the suburbs of the city. Raine shivered from the cold, matter-of-fact delivery of Colt's words. There was no loss of dignity in him. No falling over backwards with compunction. Just a firm, frank acceptance of being in the wrong. In a way, she envied that hard, impregnable self-possession of his.

'Let's forget about it,' she murmured, equally coolly.

'So he knows now,' she said conclusively to Colette a week later, having explained about the visit to Colt's stepmother and her meeting with Tim, although she had avoided mentioning that the woman he'd been involved with during their engagement had been Stephanie Falloner.

They were sitting on the beach, adorned now with the sun-baked bodies of early holiday-makers, and Raine dug her feet into the warm sand, lifting them to watch the tiny grains run between her toes.

'Colt couldn't have been more . . . different towards me since, only . . .'

'Only what?' Colette, her petiteness emphasised by a

skimpy, pink, polka-dot bikini, eyed her friend curiously. 'You
said he sent you flowers. Took you to the best restaurant on
the island. What more do you want from the man . . . blood?'

'It isn't that . . .' Raine sighed, her breasts lifting beneath the
white, one-piece swimsuit as she toyed with the strings of the
provocatively laced bodice. She wasn't sure what she was
trying to say. After all, Colt *had* changed towards her. Firstly,
with the roses. Red roses. And with no message. Just a small
white card on which he had signed his name. And she had
accepted them for what they were, a subtle apology—just as
that subequent dinner had been.

In the candlelit interior of that exclusive restaurant, she had
discovered a Colt who could make her laugh; one who shared
her liking for both classical and popular music, as well as her
own, personal aversion to too much television. He relaxed by
swimming and playing squash, he had told her, which
explained how he kept to such a peak of physical condition.
And when she had admitted to the occasional jog as her own
means of unwinding, it had been oddly warming to have his
approval. For the first time, they had met on equal
terms—without hostility—and, unlike six years ago, Raine
reflected, watching a windsurfer twisting precariously on his
board above the blue water, as woman to man. She still
couldn't help wondering why Colt hadn't ended his
relationship with Stephanie, but she hadn't been able to bring
herself to ask him again, particularly as he hadn't made any
further reference to his marriage himself. And neither of them
mentioned Tim. It was almost as if there were an unspoken
taboo on both their parts where both subjects were concerned,
and in a way Raine was glad. They had brought her enough
distress to last her a lifetime, she thought wryly now, and
undoubtedly Colt must feel the same way.

But if he had stimulated her intellectually that night, then,
physically, his very presence across the table had fanned the
flames of a desire in her she hadn't thought herself capable of.

He had aroused her with the rich, smooth warmth of his voice; with the mesmeric intensity of those beautiful eyes; by a simple contact of his hair brushing her temple when they had bent simultaneously to retrieve the key she had inadvertently dropped between their seats in the car. So, when he had come round to open the door and escort her to her flat, she had been taut with need, anticipating the reality of being crushed against him, craving his mouth on hers. But it hadn't been like that. Instead, she had had to content herself with the briefest touch of his lips on her forehead, his discerning smile making her guess that he knew how much she had wanted his kiss and was enjoying teasing her by not granting it.

'I'm crazy for him,' she murmured hopelessly, almost to herself. 'And it terrifies me.'

And after the way Colt had treated her, logic told her, she'd be very foolish getting involved with him. Even so, she couldn't help feeling disappointed when she went into the office on Monday morning to find that he wasn't in, any more than she could help the reckless leap of her heart when he rang to say that Sean was ill and asked her to collect several files, then drive out with them to his house.

'Lucky you!' the receptionist remarked, when Raine told her where she would be, her casual dismissal of Sheila's envying comment hiding a ripple of nerves. But, as she stuffed her notepad and pen into her bag, all other feelings were being over-ridden by concern for the little boy. Colt had mentioned having a housekeeper who came in every day, so Sean's condition must be serious, she suspected, for Colt not only to have kept his son on the island, but to be caring for him personally.

Quickly, she gathered together the necessary items Colt wanted, and within minutes was on the road, following the five-mile crescent of golden sand that was St Ouen's Bay. The Atlantic rollers crashing in brought the tang of salt air through the open windows of the car, the strong thunder of the current reminding Raine how dangerous the bay was except for surfing enthusiasts and really experienced swimmers. The scenery changed dramatically, however, as she drove north, bleak, open sand dunes giving way to hillier country, the road rising sharply with the towering cliffs, wild bluebells and pink willow herbs fringing the roadside as she turned into a wooded area and then off that road into the impressive, tree-canopied drive.

The house was pretty much the same as she remembered it, huge and rambling and white, overlooking its own private bay. Conifers hedged well-kept lawns and, as she stepped out of her car, she caught the stirring fragrance of wild honeysuckle.

She felt another tingle of nerves as she knocked at the front door, and her heart skipped a beat when Colt answered it himself.

'What did you do . . . fly?' His amused surprise made her conscious of how little time she had wasted in getting there, and colour tinged her cheeks as he stood aside to let her pass.

'You wanted me, so here I am,' she responded cryptically, with an effusive sweep of her arm, hoping that he wouldn't guess how she'd been propelled by a very foolish desire to please him. She breezed past him with the files under her arm, thinking how good he looked in the dark, casual shirt and light cords he was wearing and, her expression serious, she asked, 'What's the matter with Sean?'

A broad shoulder lifted, the commanding mouth twisting wryly. 'It's just a very bad tummy bug he developed yesterday. The doctor seems to think he'll be all right in a day or two, but he isn't eating a thing.'

Raine's brows drew together in sympathy. Colt looked tired, she thought, noticing the dark smudges under his eyes and the tiny creases around them. Sensitively, she asked, 'Has it been a bad night?'

He grimaced and said drily, 'You could say that. And to make matters worse, Mrs Bisson's daughter has just come home with a new baby and wants her mother, so she'll be away for a few days.'

Raine felt for him as he led her into his study, a room that was surprisingly tidy for a man with no wife, an absent housekeeper and a sick son. The desk, though, looked a shambles, with a mountain of papers strewn across it, and there were a few dead flowers in a vase on the mantelpiece. There was a book of bedtime stories and two miniature trucks, too, Raine noticed, beside it, things which she could never have imagined would have been left lying around had Stephanie been there. From her recollection of Colt's late wife, Stephanie Falloner had been house-proud to the extreme. But a vision of Colt sitting here in one of the comfortable leather armchairs with Sean on his knee, reading to him, flashed through Raine's mind; then of his carrying his son up to bed and then coming back and picking up the toys, and her throat constricted. She hadn't pictured Colt fulfilling such a domestic role, and it surprised her to realise that she liked the idea.

It was a gruelling morning, with certainly no time for social conversation. The telephone didn't stop ringing, and Colt dictated letters at a pace that made Raine suspect would have had most secretaries in tears, glad that her own shorthand speed was exceptionally high. She was transcribing on the electric typewriter he kept for his own use when he got up to make coffee and, after a few moments, she followed him out to the kitchen. It was large and sunny, with beautifully fitted oak units, and Colt was filling a glass with warm milk, presumably for Sean.

'Can I come with you?'

He was about to take it upstairs but paused, obviously surprised to see her standing there, and a smile curved his mouth when he noticed her imploring expression. 'If you want to.'

When they entered the snug little bedroom, Sean smiled weakly at his father before giving Raine a curious glance, but he was hot and feverish and, after taking a few sips of the milk, started to whimper when Colt tried to coax him to drink it all.

'Come on, son . . . you must get some nourishment inside you,' he persisted gently. And, sitting down beside Sean's pillow, he slid an arm around his shoulders.

As though that were all the inducement he needed, bravely the little boy took a few more sips, although that was all he could manage. He started whimpering again just as the telephone rang.

'I'll answer it,' Raine offered as Colt made to get up, but pretended not to hear his suggestion that she could take the call in his bedroom, feeling much more comfortable answering it in the hall.

It was Jocelyn, speaking from her brother's office in London, Raine realised, stiffening, and detected that the woman sounded rather put out at hearing Colt's secretary answering his home phone.

'Will you get him for me?' she asked, rather rudely. 'I've never liked delivering messages through typists.'

Raine bit her tongue, suppressing a surge of hot emotion as she went back upstairs to summon Colt.

'You were a long time answering it,' he commented, looking amused as he got to his feet, quite aware of how embarrssed she'd felt about going into his bedrom. She blushed, feeling ridiculous.

'I'll take over here, if you like,' she suggested, hiding her discomfiture by picking up the glass he'd set aside and sitting down beside Sean. As Colt went out of the room, she knew an unaccountable little thrill in holding the child to her. His hair was damp from where he had been perspiring, and she swept it back off his forehead, murmuring little words of comfort before suggesting she read him a story, and when Colt came back it was to find the glass almost empty on the small, white cabinet, and his son asleep against Raine's breast.

'Goodness! How did you do it?'

He looked appreciatively from the glass to the sleeping child, and then to Raine's face—framed by hair that tumbled over her shoulder like fiery silk against the pale gold of his son's—and she smiled.

'I simply told him the cows would be upset if they thought he didn't like their milk,' she answered, with an impish grin, 'and that seemed to do the trick.'

Colt moved closer to the bed, and nervously Raine licked her lips, looking up into those strong, prepossessing features. Somehow, his very nearness seemed to sap her strength, made her feel as weak and vulnerable as the child in her arms. 'You must have a natural way with children,' he commented, his mouth curling at the corners.

That dark gaze seemed to impale her, so that her voice trembled as she replied, 'We're not that much different from animals, and I've had a lot of practice in that department.' She remembered one instance in particular, when she had sat up all night with her father to nurse a sick calf. 'And that's not what you said two weeks ago,' she added, reminding him, her gaze wavering under the steady penetration of his. 'If I remember correctly, you were rather uncomplimentary about my maternal instincts.'

His mouth pulled down on one side, and she heard him curse himself softly. 'It seems I said too damn much,' he admitted in a self-deprecating tone. Then, with a sigh, 'And you haven't forgiven me yet?'

Seeing the sincere need in him for her to do so, she responded with a teasing, 'No,' and couldn't help smiling when she saw the spark of challenge that leaped in his eyes.

'Then I'll just have to try and change your mind, won't I?' he told her with equal playfulness, but the innuendo behind it made her nerve-endings quiver. As did the sound of the little single bed depressing under his weight, a movement that brought him disturbingly near. This close to him she could smell his cologne—feel the warmth emanating from him—and, uneasy beside him, she glanced down at Sean, ostensibly to gently straighten the collar of his blue-striped pyjamas.

'What made you leave the farm—Guernsey—in the first place?' Colt asked suddenly.

She shrugged. Then, without looking at him, briefly she explained her need for full independence. 'My parents are darlings, but they couldn't—still can't—accept the fact that I've grown up!' she concluded laughingly and, glancing at him then noticed how his hair shone in the sunlight from the window behind them, that there was a small nick on his chin where he must have cut himself when he'd shaved.

'Wasn't there anyone else you had second thoughts about leaving?'

He meant a boyfriend, but Raine didn't reply at once, the quiet murmur of the sea down in the bay and Sean's soft breathing filling the silence, emphasising her hesitation in answering him.

'No,' she admitted finally, lifting her chin—an unconscious gesture of rebellion which had him laughing softly.

His gaze was taking in the small boy nestled against her, the slender hand stroking the child's warm brow, and the provocative curves beneath the snug-fitting, pale blue dress, and he smiled. 'Lucky Sean,' he whispered. 'Would you give me the same comfort if I were sick?'

It was a flippant query, but Raine was shocked to realise how much she wanted to say 'yes'. And, fearing how much she was letting herself get involved with him, firmly she forced herself to remember that there were probably any number of attractive women he could call if he needed someone. Not least, the lovely Jocelyn Day. Jealousy, like a savage animal, suddenly leaped to tear at her insides with cruel claws as she pictured him with the other women and, bewildered by such a fierce emotion—unwilling, afraid to question it—she struggled to bring it under control, saying rather breathlessly, 'Are you ever sick?' One doubting glance over his broad shoulders and chest caused her stomach to turn over.

He gave a snort of disapproval. 'Believe it or not, Raine, I *am* human,' he assured her, getting up. 'And you sitting there on my son's bed is only reminding me of just how much so. So I think we'd better lay Sean down properly and get back downstairs before I start putting into practice thoughts that have nothing to do with why you're here. Here, let me.'

He was lifting Sean from her, but his fingers accidentally brushed the outer curve of her breast, and she stiffened, her breath catching in her lungs. From the questing look he sent her, he was obviously aware of that reaction in her, though he made no comment. After that, though the rest of the day passed smoothly enough, that dangerous chemistry between them had made itself felt again, leaving Raine tense and edgy, as if one were living beneath a volcano one knew would eventually erupt.

They finished work late. Colt had gone upstairs to see Sean, and Raine was just replacing the dead flowers on the mantelpiece with some budding marigolds she had seen growing outside the kitchen window, when Colt came back into the study.

'A woman's touch?'

She swung round, noticed the mocking twist to his lips, and wondered if she had been too presumptuous in picking the flowers. 'If you object, I'll . . .'

'No.' His lips compressed as he moved towards her, his feet making no sound on the deeply carpeted floor. 'I approve. And Sean's asking to see you before you leave. It seems you've scored quite a hit with him.'

Raine swallowed as he came to stand just in front of her, his nearness making what she intended to say much more difficult. But she wanted to help him, to alleviate the difficulties of his coping alone, lend some comfort to the motherless little boy; shifting her weight from one foot to the other, she uttered uncomfortably, 'I—I could stay if you wanted me to.' There, it was out. But the mockery in Colt's eyes made her feel even more awkward—wonder if she should have said anything.

His hands on her shoulders caused her pulse to race. 'Thanks,' he said wryly, 'but I've got a sick son to handle, and I think you'd be a distraction I'd be best doing without.'

The casual touch of his hands was far too stimulating through her thin dress and, her mouth dry, she said tartly, 'I was offering my services . . . not myself,' embarrassed that he should have interpreted her suggestion in any other way.

'I know,' he surprised her by responding, looking down into her indignant features. 'But do you really think we could spend the night here alone together without winding up in the same bed?'

'Yes,' she said, her chin asserting itself, and she saw one thick, tawny eyebrow arch in obvious scepticism.

'If you think that, my dear child, then you're pretending to yourself as well as me,' he told her admonishingly, his hands, sliding down her bare arms, causing little tingles to shiver along her spine. 'Every time I come within a foot of you, I get a signal that's stronger than all the aphrodisiacs and love potions put together.'

'You're imagining things!' She tried to laugh, sick at herself for not being able to conceal her feelings the way he could, and annoyed at him for being able to tell so easily.

His smile was discerning. 'Oh, no, I'm not,' he breathed softly, and drew her towards him, making her blood race through her. His lips brushed her hairline—warm and sensual—that musky, male scent of him stripping her of her sensibilities. Under her hands, his heartbeat was regular and strong, unlike hers, which screamed like a captured bird. She was swaying towards him, every impulse of her enslaved femininity crying out for his kiss—the ecstasy of his caresses. But he was putting her from him, saying stoically, 'You're giving off that signal now, and you're coming very close to making me do something about it, so I think the sooner you get yourself off home, the better.'

Not needing to be told a second time, she pulled away from him, keeping her head averted so that he wouldn't see the disappointment in her face, and going straight upstairs to see Sean.

The little boy was still awake and, straightening his duvet, she kissed him goodnight, and felt a little tug on her heart-strings when he queried entreatingly, 'Are you coming back again tomorrow?'

'Yes,' Raine promised smilingly, ruffling his hair, and was pleased to discover that he felt less feverish than he had earlier.

He would soon be better, she thought gratefully when she was driving home, which meant that there wouldn't be too many more days when she would have to go to Colt's house. His attraction for her had got too strong a hold on her, she warned herself, and yet silently she couldn't help questioning, why, when Colt had been so determined initially to make her pay with her surrender to him, he was showing such amazing restraint now. It wasn't because he no longer wanted her, she accepted, crunching gears in her agitation, because every stray glance, every touch, however casual, told her that he did. Therefore, she could only reach the assumption that what Tim had said was true, that she wasn't his brother's type, intellectually, anyway. And she guessed that, now Colt wasn't seeking to hurt her any more, he'd probably be looking for physical gratification with someone more sophisticated, like Jocelyn Day.

The thought speared her but, cutting the engine, Raine tried telling herself, quite adamantly, that she didn't care. After all, what was he to her, other than her employer? she thought, half angrily, letting herself into the flat. But even so, her slumber was filled with erotic dreams of him that night, and she woke from the strength of her longing to find that it was still dark, and that her pillow was damp with tears.

It was two days before Sean was well enough to get up.

Raine drove out to the house each morning, and then plunged herself headlong into the work Colt gave her, only answering him briefly when he tried to draw her into conversation, reluctant to acknowledge the warm feelings that surged through her whenever he smiled at her in a certain way. She was afraid of what she might be getting herself into, afraid of getting hurt. And he seemed content to leave her to her reticence at first—submerged in work himself—so that it came as rather a surprise to her when he strode into the study on the third afternoon and, with a deprecating look at the typewriter, ordered, 'Turn that thing off. I'm taking Sean out for some air, and he's specially requested that you come with us.'

Raine's immediate response was to protest, telling him that she had too much to do. But he was insisting, and rather tentatively she obeyed, wondering how much the invitation had to do with the little boy, or if his father had had some influence regarding it.

What did it matter? she told herself firmly, annoyed to find herself hoping that it had been Colt's wish, too, although she was warmed by the child running up to her and catching her hand as she followed his father out to the car.

It was an ideal day—still, sunny and warm—and surprisingly Raine found herself relaxing with Colt as he pulled out of the drive and on to the road, put at ease by his light, casual conversation. They hadn't gone very far though, before he was swinging the car off the road again and along a narrow track fringed by trees on one side and high hedges on the other.

'I've made a recent acquisition,' he told her, seeing the query in her eyes. With an almost mischievous grin, he added, 'As a farmer's daughter, I thought you might be interested.'

Raine looked at him curiously, but he wasn't saying any more, and she had to wait until he pulled up beside a five-bar gate before he said, 'Come and look.'

Sean was already clambering on to the gate's decaying woodwork when she reached it to look at what Colt was show-

ing her. The land beyond it joined his own. She could see the
house with its gardens and lawns from here. But immediately
in front of them were acres of open pasture, the few
slumbering buildings and outbuildings dotted across it and the
twenty or so quietly grazing cattle presenting a peaceful scene
in the warm afternoon sun.

Raine laughed her amazement as things suddenly became
clear. 'You mean . . . you've bought a farm!' Her eyes glistened
their surprise. What would he want with that?

He grinned again, amused by her astonishment, a warm
satisfaction in the strong features as he gazed proudly over his
new property. 'No, I'm not going to develop the land,' he
assured her, as the question darted fleetingly through her
mind. 'I need something to escape the pressure of work
sometimes, and what better way than by getting entirely back
to nature? Obviously, someone else is managing it for me, but
in time I'd like to be more actively involved. Spend less time
away from home with development ventures and spend more
here—build a more solid home-life for Sean.'

And that was more important to him than anything, Raine
realised, respecting him for that more than she would ever
have been prepared to let him know.

He was helping Sean over the little stile beside the gate and,
with one agile movement, had crossed it himself. Raine's pulse
quickened as he turned and held out his hand to help her over.

She took it, one step down bringing her almost into his
arms, and she caught her breath, the coarseness of his denim
shirt beneath the hand she shot out to steady herself making
her body rife with sensation. He smiled down at her instant
withdrawal, knowing exactly how she was feeling. Damn him!
she thought, as they strode after Sean, who had already darted
away.

The cows were munching peacefully as they approached,
large brown eyes lifting to the three newcomers without any
sign of alarm. Having been brought up on a farm, Raine was

used to them, and gently she stroked the warm golden coat of one of them, laughing as it turned a huge pink nose towards her, the almost fawnlike features placid and trusting.

'They're the most beautiful cattle in the world, aren't they?' They were a symbol of the islands, and she was proud of them. Her eyes were shining with emotion as she looked up at Colt. 'Our Guernseys are larger than these, but they're pretty much the same,' she told him, stroking the animal's soft muzzle.

Beside her, she heard Colt chuckle. 'Well, they would be, wouldn't they?' He laughed at her puzzled frown, his teeth white against his tan. 'You mean, you've lived here all your life and don't know what's probably one of your islands' oldest customs?'

She shrugged, wishing that she could say she did, but she didn't. 'You'll have to enlighten me, professor,' she responded playfully.

Her spirited remark brought a glitter to his eyes that told her he would like to do a lot more than that, but at least he complied. 'The similarity, Raine,' he said soberly, patting the creature's back, 'arises because in the old days, when a Jersey farmer's daughter married a Guernseyman . . .' his lips compressed '. . . or the other way around, she would take him a calf as part of her dowry.'

'What a quaint idea,' Raine laughed, and vaguely remembered her father telling her something like that once. 'Do you think it will catch on again?' she added, with impish scepticism.

Colt grinned. 'Probably not,' he accepted. 'Although *I* like to think that originally it signified that she was prepared to mix blood . . . and not just with their cattle.' Raine looked at him questioningly, and noticed the lop-sided smile he flashed her. With his eyes holding hers, very softly he said, 'She was offering her body to create new life with him . . . to bear *his* children.'

Absurdly, she blushed, finding that she couldn't look away

from those beautiful eyes. The quiet gurgling of a nearby stream and the soft munching of the cattle were sounds in a distant world, the pull of that strong, sexual chemistry anaesthetising her to everything but the warmth tingling through her, which had nothing to do with the sun on her bare arms. She seemed transfixed by that gaze, and awkwardly she laughed again to break the tension which was like an electric charge on the air between them.

'Colston Falloner . . . you're a romantic at heart!'

His mouth pulled down one side. 'Don't accuse me of that!' he laughed, but there was a cynical edge to his voice. Even so, it couldn't chill the sea of warm emotion flowing through Raine. Absently, she heard Sean call to them from some way off, heard Colt's suggestion that they follow him. And in a daze she walked beside him, realising that there was another Colt beneath that tough, invincible shell he presented to the world. In the past few days she had seen him as a warm and caring human being, though she guessed there was probably a lot more to him that she couldn't even begin to guess at. But, startlingly, she had only just realised something about herself. Incredibly—crazily!—she was falling in love with him.

# CHAPTER SEVEN

THE days passed in a heady whirl for Raine and, back at the office, keeping her mind on her work was even more difficult that it had been before, though for a different reason now. Since the discovery of her feelings for Colt, she found herself trembling every time he looked at her. The simplest praise from him could make her pulses throb with pleasure, and hopelessly she realised that she was living now solely for the hours when she could be in his company.

As for Colt, he seemed to be doing his utmost to make up for the way he had misjudged her. He took her to lunch regularly, often boosting her morale by asking her advice on some problem he was dealing with in the office—at least, that was what she decided he was doing, because she didn't think there would be any problem that that brilliant brain of his couldn't tackle alone. Then there was the odd red rose she would discover on her typewriter sometimes, after he had gone out. And, very occasionally, he would ask her out to dinner. Yet, when he took her home on those heart-singing occasions, he was courteous in the extreme, the light brush of his lips over hers, or a mere brotherly peck on her cheek, doing nothing to slake the hunger for him which was growing stronger in her with each passing day. Only making love with him, she accepted despairingly, could do that. But he seemed reluctant now to share more than a platonic relationship with her, and miserably Raine reminded herself that he was simply being nice to her and taking her out because he still felt bad about the way he had treated her, while she was falling deeper and deeper in love with him. And, as if she didn't have enough to complicate her life, she started receiving telephone calls from Tim.

'I rang you yesterday,' he started by saying as soon as Sheila put his call through, 'but they said you'd gone out to lunch with *him*.' His derogatory tone made it abundantly clear to Raine what he thought of her lunching with his brother. 'I thought there wasn't anything going on between you two.'

'There isn't,' Raine snapped, silently wishing she could have said otherwise. 'And if there was, it wouldn't be any of your business, anyway.' She guessed that, in his new unemployed state, Tim probably had nothing better to do, although she was well aware that he'd thrown in his own job with his brother's associate company—Colt hadn't actually been cold-blooded enough to fire him—and a warmth tingled through her, a respect as deep as her new-found love. 'Colt wanted me to help him choose some books for Sean,' she went on, remembering how flattered she had been that he had asked her. 'You know, your *nephew,*' she bit out caustically, gathering from things Colt had said that his brother seldom showed any interest in the little boy.

'If that's supposed to be hinting at what I think it is,' Tim snarled in response, 'the kid's never liked me, anyway.'

She had gathered that, too, from the way Sean had shrunk back from his uncle at his grandmother's that day. And if she herself had been hoping she'd seen the last of Tim, with dismay she realised that he had other ideas when he suddenly asked her out.

It was an effort to stop herself saying something very rude to him, but she managed it, very politely, but firmly, telling him that she wasn't interested, although she was finding the conversation thoroughly embarrassing because Jack Hardwicke had come out of his office and was rummaging through the filing cabinet, looking rather amused, obviously thinking she was having problems with some intractable boyfriend, she thought, annoyed. But her blunt refusal to see Tim didn't put him off, because he rang again the next day, several times, the last only minutes after Colt had come out and dictated a letter to her before dashing out to see a client. Raine was grateful for that, at least. She didn't relish the idea of having to do battle with her ex-fiancé while Colt was in earshot!

She was surprised, therefore, when Sheila came up just as she was slamming the receiver down on Tim for what she decided would be the final time, and the receptionist remarked, 'What's wrong with Colston? Doesn't he like calls being put through to you while he's around? Or is it just his brother he objects to you speaking to?' And, seeing Raine's puzzled look, went on, 'He was in reception when I put Tim Falloner through to you, and wanted to know if he'd spoken to you before.' She deposited herself on the edge of Raine's desk, a tight-fitting mini skirt exposing a good deal of shapely leg. 'When I said he had—about four times so far this week—he didn't look too pleased.' She grimaced. 'In fact, if he'd been coming in just now instead of going out, from the expression on his face he might well have flown up here and horse-whipped you!' The receptionist sucked in her breath. 'Quite something when he's angry, isn't he?'

Yes, he was, Raine admitted silently, with an unwelcome tug of something deep down inside. But, as the other girl moved away, she pondered over why Colt should be so angry about Tim ringing her. Foolishly, a small sliver of hope started her wondering if he might possibly be jealous. Because if he were, wouldn't that mean that he cared a little?

She got a grip on her emotions right there. Of course he didn't care, she forced herself to accept, painful though it was. And, if she carried on the way she was going, she knew she would only wind up with a broken heart. Consequently, when Colt returned and invited her out to dinner that night, at first she refused, and it was only a combination of his persuasiveness, and her own longing to be with him, that eventually had her accepting.

'I hear Tim's been phoning you,' he surprised her by saying suddenly after they had finished their dessert that evening.

Across the table, Raine watched the movement of his hand as he stirred his black coffee, wondering why he'd waited so long to bring the subject up. Perhaps it wasn't that important to him, and Sheila had been mistaken when she'd said that he'd looked angry . . .

'Yes,' she admitted; looking up, she could read nothing from his expression.

'What does he want?'

Raine shrugged, her gaze unconsciously sweeping over the broad shoulders beneath the grey velvet jacket. 'For us to get back together, I imagine.'

Colt's eyes were hooded as they raked over her face, then rested on the simple black silk dress, the bodice of which was draped across the bust from a gold shoulder motif, emphasising the fullness of her breasts. 'Is there any chance of that happening?' he asked, his tone as detached as he seemed to appear.

Sipping a liqueur, Raine was about to offer an immediate denial, then stopped herself. If he had the slightest inkling of where her feelings really lay, he would probably be amused, she realised hopelessly. If he knew that every waking moment she spent thinking about *him* . . . Playing for time, she sent a glance across the small, intimate restaurant.

It was almost twilight outside, so that the little pink lamps on each table were coming into their own, throwing a warm blush over the vase of coloured carnations on each crisp, white cloth, while in one corner of the room, on a small circle of floorspace, one or two couples were swaying to some slow and dreamy live music.

Turning back to Colt and, striving to bring some uncertainty to her voice, she murmured, 'I wouldn't think so.'

His eyes probed hers. 'You were in love with him once.'

*Yes, but before I really knew you!* her heart cried, because she knew now that she had never really loved Tim, not in the way that she loved his brother, and wanted him to love her. The futility of her emotions brought a pained looked to her eyes and, hearing Colt catch his breath, she glanced up curiously.

'Couldn't we talk about something else?' she suggested, keen to steer him away from the topic of her own feelings. And was startled when his cup clattered noisily into its saucer and he stood up, reaching for her, his hard fingers encircling her wrist.

'Yes, let's dance.'

It was like being branded by him as he pulled her into his arms, pressing her so hard against him that the heat of his body seemed to sear hers through the flimsy dress. She had made him angry by being deliberately evasive, she realised, and with a surge of hope she wondered if she had been right earlier in thinking that he was jealous.

But the long, lean hardness of him against her was producing sensations in her that were making her tremble and, afraid that he would notice, she murmured breathlessly, 'I didn't want to dance. Let go of me.'

Her request had the reverse effect, and his arms were suddenly tightening around her. She gave a small gasp, brought into contact with every solid muscle of his masculinity, and above her she heard him groan his satisfaction.

'You know, your eyes turn a deep emerald when you're aroused, Raine.' His tone was low, velvety soft, turning her blood to fire. 'Are you aroused now?'

'No,' she breathed, hating him for what he could do to her, but the huskiness of her voice made mockery of her denial.

'No?' he challenged, holding her away from him a little so that he could look at her, his eyes taking in the flush on her cheeks, the dilated pupils, the trembling fullness of her parted lips. All she could do was shut her eyes against the betrayal of her emotions, the warm cognisance of his smile.

The music had taken on an almost erotic flavour so that, as he pulled her back to him, they seemed to move to the slow rhythm as one. In a sensual daze, she remembered the first time she had danced with him, when she had used her love for Tim as a shield against that first, unwelcome tug of attraction; only now there was nothing to protect her from it, and this time he was showing her no restraint. He was aroused and he was letting her know it, his chest crushing her breasts, his thighs moving intimately against hers. For a while, in the security of the restaurant, she allowed herself to drown in the scent, the sound, the feel of him, totally oblivious to the music, the murmur of conversation, and the other couples dancing around them.

'Let's get out of here.' From a distance, it seemed, Colt's voice sounded hoarse—as if he were having difficulty drawing breath—and, unmindful of anything but him, she allowed him to lead her away, wondering why she couldn't find anything to say to him as she sat beside him in the sleek, silver saloon while he drove like a madman along the dark country lanes.

When he pulled up outside her flat, she murmured a swift 'thank you' and made to get out, knowing that, even if she was being rude, for the sake of the continuing function of her senses she had to get away from him. But she was seconds too late. He was reaching for her, a naked hunger in his eyes and, in defiance of every barrier she had erected against him, every feminine cell screamed out to him in response.

Sensations rocketed through her as he pulled her down across his lap, and when he covered her mouth with his it was like the earth exploding, every element blending in a shattering eruption of fire and water and air.

Oh, God! It had been so long since he had kissed her! She was like a mad thing in his arms, as wild for him as he was for her, meeting the fierceness of his kiss with a passion that brought her straining towards him, her body jerking in a spasm of intense need as he found her breast and moulded it to his palm. Her breathing was as ragged as his, sharp fingers of desire clawing at her loins as his hands ran over her body so that she had to stifle her small cries in the soft velvet of his shoulder, not knowing how she could take any more of this torturous wanting without the ultimate conclusion of his possession.

He caught her to him with a deep groan that signified his immense effort for control, and then his fingers found the key she was clutching so tightly, took it from her and, with a gentle firmness, his voice husky with emotion, he murmured, 'Come on.'

She wanted to tell him that she wasn't protected, that she could get pregnant if they made love. But she wanted him so much that she couldn't have borne his rejection of her, and blindly she let him lead her to the flat, too raw with need to say anything.

He was reaching for her almost before he'd closed the door behind them, finding her ready for him, the short interruption in their lovemaking having only heightened her arousal from the thought of what he intended to do. She was burning up with a fever for him, the fierce domination of his mouth and hands, and the feel, the scent and taste of him driving her delirious.

'Oh, God!' His agonised groan came as she tugged his shirt out of his waistband, knew the thrill of running her fingers over the hard, flexing muscles of his chest, and he was unzipping her dress, letting it fall, so that she was naked save for a pair of lacy black briefs as he swept her up into his arms. Somehow, by the time he laid her down on her bed, she had unbuttoned his shirt so that that strong, tanned chest was looming over her, and little darts of anticipation and excitement arrowed through her. His features were in shadow, but moonlight from the window threw a shaft of silver across the bed, across the fiery cascade of auburn against the pillow, showing him eyes that were glazed with desire, cheeks which were flushed, the gentle beams bathing her throat and breasts creamy-white in the soft light. And, as Colt bent to kiss the hardened peak of one and then looked up at her with dark, slumbrous eyes, she could see his face clearly and thought that he looked like a man who had just found heaven.

'You're beautiful,' he whispered. 'So beautiful.' Each word was punctuated with little kisses over the full swell of her breasts. And for the first time in her life she was pleased with her generous curves, because she knew that the most important thing to her now was pleasing Colt—that she had been born for that purpose—and she told herself that at least she was as much a woman as any he had made love to in the past. Well, almost, she reasoned vaguely, with a small twinge of anxiety towards the unknown, because it would take Colt to finally turn her into a complete woman.

She watched him remove his own clothes and come back to her, a superb specimen of masculinity, fit and muscular and tanned, and she caught her breath as he removed her last flimsy garment, as the thrilling warmth of his nakedness met the inviting softness of hers. Her hands revelled in the feel of that strong, hard body, tentative at first, but then with growing confidence, although they were unpractised compared with his. With the proficiency of a master he drove her mindless for him, using not only his hands but his voice, his lips and his tongue until she was begging him for release. Then she was alive to nothing but his sliding into her, the quick, sharp pain and his hesitancy, then the blinding, driving ecstasy as he finally lost control. And a long time later, when she was lying in his arms, with her head against the damp warmth of his shoulder, he said quietly, 'Why didn't you tell me I would be the first?'

Her tongue tasting the slight saltiness of his skin, Raine swallowed. Was he angry with her?

'Does it matter?'

He moved, leaning on an elbow to look down into her face,

his profile strong even in the semi-darkness. 'No, I'd just have been more gentle with you if I'd known. But I thought that, if no one else, then surely you and Tim . . .' He sounded amazed, and Raine shook her head, and smiling up at him wondered how any man could have been more considerate. 'Oh, my beautiful girl.' His hands, softly caressing her again, were arousing in their tenderness. 'I want you.' He bent to kiss her, slowly, sensuously, and she felt new desire stir in him and in herself. 'Live with me, Raine. Move in with me. Tomorrow. First thing.'

Her breath seemed to lock in her chest, and she looked at him questioningly, her eyes wide. 'Just like that?' She didn't know what to say, totally nonplussed by his request. 'Colt, I can't. I . . .'

'Why not?' He caught her chin between his thumb and fore-finger, turning her averted face to his. 'Is it what your parents will say that's worrying you?'

She could never get over how well he could read her mind, because she had just been thinking that her parents would probably die of shock if she announced that she was going to live with a man, although that wasn't the reason that she couldn't bring herself to agree to what he was suggesting. The only thing that was stopping her was that she loved him too much to become just another of his affairs, to live with the insecurity of knowing that one day it would all have to end . . .

And, before she had time to say anything, he was pulling her round to face him, his voice husky as he asked, 'Do you want *me?*'

'Yes.'

'Do you want this?' Demonstratively, his hand cupped her breast, his thumb teasing the rosy peak until it hardened and she groaned her admission. And suddenly he was moving to pin her beneath him, his eyes flickering with a dark emotion as he said, 'Well, I want you . . . any way I can get you . . . and if it takes a minor legality to keep you in my bed, then marry me,

Raine.'

She stared up at him open-mouthed, her eyes disbelieving. He was asking her to marry him and she was *hesitating*? A spring of joy suddenly burst in her—flooded into her heart—and breathlessly she was murmuring, 'Are you saying you love me, Colt?'

'No.' His truthful response stemmed the warmth in her veins, and his lips pulled to one side when he felt her tangible withdrawal. 'That word is used far too liberally. Causes too many people too much suffering. I know. I've been there before. I'm a realist, Raine. But I know I want you. Want to take you to bed each night and drive you wild for me. And when I wake up in the morning, find that you're still beside me. Still mine. I can't bear the thought of anyone else ever having you.'

It wasn't the most romantic proposal in the world, and the depth of his possessiveness made her shudder. It was an impetuous decision, too, she felt, and quite out of character for him, she knew him well enough to realise. But he wasn't committing himself fully emotionally and, with knitted brows, she found herself asking, 'Can I think about it?'

The hands which had been idly caressing her stilled, and she heard him catch his breath. 'If you need to,' he accepted raggedly, those strong features seeming oddly vulnerable in the dim light. 'Only don't take too long.'

She didn't. During the next couple of days, she turned his proposal over and over in her mind, trying to imagine what her life would be like if he wasn't part of it now, and it didn't bear thinking about. Only she wished he'd given her more time. She knew she loved him, knew it was ridiculous even questioning whether he loved her. After all, he was asking her to marry him, wasn't he? she chided herself silently. To make a lifelong commitment? And he was hardly an inexperienced youth confusing love with physical desire. So why was she so afraid?

It didn't take much working out for her to realise that it was because of Tim. She'd been hurt badly before, and she wanted to be absolutely certain of her partner before deciding on such a big step again. And Colt wasn't laying his emotions open. But then, hadn't he been hurt badly, too? she reminded herself, understanding his reluctance—his fear, perhaps—to do so. Therefore, wouldn't it be up to the two of them to make the relationship work—up to *her* to show *him* that he could fully trust a woman again? Well, she would, she resolved, humming a little tune as she got herself ready for bed. And the following morning, in the privacy of his office, she gave him her answer.

They were married two weeks later in the little church they could see from the house. *Their* house, Raine mused warmly, trying to get used to the idea as she stepped out into the sunshine to be met by showers of confetti and congratulations from the few guests who had been invited. She had chosen a straight, elegant wedding gown in cream, since she considered white too stark for her fair complexion. Her only attendant—Sean—was in blue velvet, looking very important as a page. She felt Colt's arm curl possessively around her now, and as she looked at him, her face aglow with pleasure and pride, her stomach did a little somersault when she read the naked desire in his eyes.

I love you, hers said silently, before she heard the small oath he uttered and realised, with a small cloud over her happiness, that the Press had somehow got to hear of their marriage and were waiting outside the church gates.

'Mr Falloner, is it true that Mrs Falloner used to be engaged to your brother?'

Ignoring the blatant question, Colt steered Raine out of the reporter's way, but the man was coming after them.

'How did he take the news of the two of you marrying?' A camera flashed. 'Is he here today, sir?'

He wasn't, not having been informed of their wedding, but

Colt was saying nothing, his mouth grim, and Raine was grateful for his cool composure as he handed her into the waiting car. She turned away from another flash of the camera, breathing a sigh of relief when Colt got in and put the vehicle into motion, cursing under his breath.

'Don't worry.' He gave her a reassuring smile as they sped away from the church. 'They'll have forgotten all about us in a week or so, though I suppose it was inevitable that they'd find out.'

Yes, it was, Raine thought, with her husband being such a big name on the island. *Her husband.* It felt good, and she smiled to herself, hugging the feeling secretly to her.

There was a small reception at the house, the hour or so they spent there passing in a sea of felicitations—a kiss from Jack Hardwicke, from Colette and the bearded young man at her side. And then John Welland was hugging her daughter; Joan was small and elegant in a green dress and jacket, her short, fiery hair the only obvious feature she had passed on to Raine.

'Well, one Falloner certainly had no intention of letting you get away,' John Welland, tall and spruce beside his wife, remarked rather drily, reminding Raine how both he and her mother had been shocked at first by Colt's intention to marry her so soon. But that was before they had met him, she thought, smiling as she kissed her father's strong cheek, because at Colt's invitation her parents had spent the past week with him and, like everyone, were won over by his charm almost immediately. His farming interests had made her father a firm ally, Raine realised, although only after he'd established that his daughter wasn't pregnant. She could laugh now at how mortified she'd been when when he'd challenged Colt quite openly about it, remembering how unperturbed he'd been himself, putting her parents' minds at rest with an amused diplomacy she had marvelled at.

'I'm so glad.' Ruth Falloner was beside her, tears in her eyes as she kissed Colt's bride on the cheek. 'I didn't think any woman would ever be able to pin him down again, but you've got what it takes, dear, and I'm pleased for you both.'

It was a 'welcome to the family', and Raine's eyes shone her gratitude. 'I'll try to make him happy,' she whispered and, looking up, met her husband's gaze across the room. There was a look of possession in the eyes that held hers—a silent message of wanting and need and desire. Go and change, those eyes said, and she obeyed, slipping quietly away, a quiver of excitement sending a wonderful warmth through her.

He hadn't made love to her since the night he had proposed, telling her, teasingly, that he wanted their wedding night to be meaningful. In actual fact, he'd said he hadn't wanted physical desire to influence her decision to marry him, and then, when she had accepted, they had had little time together, with him going away for a few days on business and then her parents arriving. The last two weeks had been lost in a whirlwind of wedding preparations, shopping and planning. And when she and Colt had managed to snatch a few moments alone, it had been he who had called a halt to their stolen lovemaking, exercising an amazing control, saying that when he made love to her again it would be unhurried, with no time limits, and no likelihood of being interrupted . . . She was tingling with a feverish excitement as, in a simple peach cotton suit and white blouse, she went downstairs, anticipating the night that was now only hours away. On the bottom stair, though, she paused, hearing voices coming from Colt's study. And oddly, one was angry, at that. Colt's voice was low—signifying that immense control—yet so low that she couldn't make out what he was saying. But it was the other man's voice she had heard raised, and she stiffened now, recognising it.

'Oh, I agree she's got the body of a sex goddess, but she's not quite the sophisticated woman of the world you usually knock around with, is she? So why did you marry her, Colt?'

Tim? Here? And talking about *her*? She moved nearer to the door which was slightly ajar, her throat going dry, wondering what Colt would say.

'It was just to get even with me, wasn't it?' the resentful voice continued. 'Come on, let me hear you deny it.'

Raine's nails were digging into her palms, but she couldn't explain why she was so tense. Of course Colt would deny it!

She heard him say something, but didn't catch what it was. Then the clink of a glass told her that he had moved over to the drinks cabinet just behind the door, and when he spoke again Raine's blood seemed to freeze in her veins, because this time there was no mistaking what he said. 'Well, isn't it a fair exchange, Tim? Raine for Stephanie? You must admit, it's a good way of avenging myself knowing how much *you* wanted her, and from your obvious objection to my marriage, it's worked beautifully.'

She couldn't believe she was hearing this! With a choked sob, she clamped her hands over her ears, then dragged them down again, reluctant, yet compelled, to keep listening.

'. . . why else would I have married her, other than to gloat about my victory every time I took her?' Colt's voice continued, controlled and remorseless, searing through the heart of his new bride like a laser. Her face lined with anguish, she leaned closer to the gap, but then suddenly the door was slammed shut and all she could hear was a muffled response from Timothy and then a fierce growl from Colt. Repressed sobs caught painfully in her chest, so that it was difficult to breathe. No wonder he hadn't told her he loved her! At least he hadn't been hypocritical or dishonest about that.

One hysterical sound rose in her throat as she moved quickly away, stumbling blindly up the stairs, battling against a tearing, emotional torture. So her husband had only married her for revenge! All that hatred that had been channelled against her in the beginning he had now turned on Tim; only, now she was the innocent sacrifice—a symbol of victory in the struggle for masculine supremacy between the two men. And his marrying her hadn't been an impetuous decision, she realised now, but a cold, calculated act. God! How he must have loved Stephanie! she thought, her heart breaking as desperately she sought the privacy of the bedroom she had just left, for time to bring her emotions back under control.

No longer the happy girl who had tripped lightly out of there only minutes before, she flung the door shut against the reality of the conversation she had just overheard, ramming her clenched fist into her mouth to stop herself from crying out. If Colt heard her distress, he'd come up and want to know what was wrong, and she'd have to explain, and she couldn't—wouldn't be able to—not yet. She was too shaken even to think properly, let alone speak; the only thing her mind was capable of registering was that, through some cruel irony, history was repeating itself. Again her hopes of fulfilment with a Falloner man had been dashed before they'd even begun, only this time the pain was greater than anything she had suffered through Tim. That had been bad enough. She'd thought at the time that she could never know such hurt again, but that adolescent love for Timothy had been nothing compared to this earth-shattering emotion she felt for Colt. This time the pain was killing, and she didn't know how she was ever going to live through it.

She started as someone knocked on the door, and quickly she brushed at her tears with trembling fingers. 'Who is it?' Was that her voice—that barely audible croak?

'Colt. May I come in?'

'No!' Panic forced the sudden cry from her and she sucked in her breath, hoping he hadn't detected anything wrong, adding quickly, 'Don't be impatient. I'm not dressed yet.' She forced herself to sound calm—even managed a tremulous little laugh. 'I'll be down in a minute.'

From behind the door, she heard him chuckle. 'Modesty, sweetheart? I would have thought that a rather lapsed virtue.' Amusement laced the deep tones. 'All right, darling. I can wait. For the time being.'

His remark sent a cruel dart of pain arrowing through her. How could he, after what she'd just heard him saying to Tim? She felt sick with misery, but his footsteps *were* retreating and she was grateful for that at least. Trying to compose herself before following him, she wondered what she should do. Go down and confront him right away? Tell him what she had heard? And what then? How would she tell the guests who were still celebrating her marriage that the whole thing had been a mistake? Because that was what she would have to do.

And yet, when she went downstairs—a sick feeling in the pit of her stomach—she lost her nerve, unable to challenge him in front of anyone else. And if she'd been considering confronting him alone, then when she saw her father's proud smile as she appeared, took her mother's tearful hug with a lump in her throat, she knew that she couldn't say anything then that would result in hurting them. Numbly, she took their good wishes with a smile pasted on her lips. There was no sign of Tim, nor did anyone mention him to her, and outside, as Ruth Falloner kissed her, Raine wondered what the woman would say when she eventually learned that her stepson's marriage was a farce—solely an act of revenge.

Cold with misery, she sat beside Colt as he drove them to the airstrip and his own private plane, and, pain gnawing at her, she tried not to think of the three-day honeymoon they had planned in southern France which she had anticipated with such joy and excitement. Her hands were clenched tightly in her lap.

She almost jumped when Colt said suddenly, softly, 'We had a visitor while you were upstairs changing . . . Tim.'

She stiffened and, keeping her gaze fixed on the windscreen, felt the glance her husband sliced her way. But then he was reaching for her hand, slipping his fingers through hers to lift it to his lips, his kiss so dangerously stimulating—so sensual against the sensitive skin of her wrist—that she caught her breath.

'Don't you want to know what he wanted?'

Raine's throat constricted. Of course, she should have asked that. Her heart came up into her mouth, every nerve tensing as she uttered, 'What *did* he want?'

'You, I think, dearest.' While he spoke, he was looking at the road but, when she darted him a stealthy glance from under her lashes, she was disconcerted to meet the hard amber of his gaze—warm, but intense, assessing.

She looked away, her face paling. 'And what did you tell him?' It was a job keeping her voice steady. She felt his cursory glance over her again, but this time she didn't look at him.

'That you were mine now . . . and I'm keeping you.' It was almost an admission, though not quite, but there was no mistaking the possessive tightening of his hand over hers as he lifted it to his lips again. 'And here we are . . .'

They had reached the airstrip and Raine sat back in her seat, relaxing a little in defeat. And yet she despised herself for not having had the courage to confront him with the truth then. The opportunity had been there and she had let it slide, too cowardly to face up to hearing what he would say. Of course, he'd probably try and deny having said it, though heaven only knew how he could! she thought, being led like a zombie to the waiting plane. But, if he didn't, what would she do? Leave him? she wondered abjectly. Misery filled her as she considered the prospect of living without him—never seeing him again. Chillingly, she realised that the papers would have a field day if they could report that the girl who had jilted one Falloner only two weeks before the wedding, and then married his brother, had also run out on *him* immediately afterwards.

She couldn't remember what she said to him on that flight, feeling his presence beside her like a stranger's. Yet, oddly, she had implicit trust in his handling of the plane, and they reached their hotel shortly before dinner, arriving in a taxi which had met them at the airstrip. Raine watched Colt sign in, and with mounting apprehension allowed him to take her arm as they followed the concierge, who showed them up to their room. Or, rather, suite!

Highly glossed white doors with brass trimmings led off the ornate-ceilinged and thickly carpeted lounge, the extent of Colt's wealth being obvious from the unmitigated luxury he was lavishing upon her with this honeymoon.

*Honeymoon!* Raine shuddered, wondering what he would say when she told him he wasn't going to get one—because her pride wouldn't let her sleep with him now—and she found she was trembling as she went into the next room and saw the enormity of the imposing double bed.

She started as Colt came up behind her, as his arms went around her, pulling her against him.

'Surely you're not nervous, darling?' There was amusement and surprise in the deep voice, awareness in every inch of him. He pressed his lips against the nape of her neck, his kiss sending traitorous little tingles down her spine, his hands sliding up across her breasts so that, unbidden, a flame of treacherous desire leaped in her, and she heard him murmur his appreciation as he felt their instantaneous response.

Dear God! she thought. How can he still do this to me after what I found out today? She uttered a small sound—a protest —but he mistook it for ardour, turning her round in his arms.

'Do you want to miss dinner?' His voice was husky, his eyes dark with wanting, and Raine gazed up at him, momentarily paralysed by the pure masculine beauty of his features. The glimmering suggestion of fire in his hair as he bent his head; the proud sweep of his forehead, hard cheekbone and jaw; the dark length of lashes half veiling the hunger in those amber eyes, and that cruel mouth, all amounting to a sensuality so dangerous to her that it threatened whatever scrap of immunity she had against him—the gossamer-fine shell of her self-respect.

'No, I . . .' Tension etched the perfect structure of her own, more delicately boned features, a line appearing between the guarded emerald of her eyes. She had to tell him now.

Her throat constricted, dry as a scorched desert. 'Colt, I don't . . .'

A knock at the door cut short her nervous attempt to say anything, and after the delivery of champagne, when Colt had tipped the concierge and poured the sparkling wine, Raine put the long-stemmed glass to her trembling lips, finding that once again her courage had failed her.

Fortunately, Colt didn't pursue any further suggestion of missing dinner, but downstairs, in the romantically lit restaurant with its dimmed chandeliers and intimately spaced tables, Raine found herself with little appetite, knowing that her time was running out.

'Would you like to dance?'

She didn't, but they had finished their meal and she wanted to stall the inevitable moment of confrontation for as long as possible, and so she agreed, realising that that was totally foolish as soon as Colt's arms went around her. The music was soft and beautiful, the perfect prelude to seduction, she thought achingly, her heart crying out for what might have been, the lilting notes of the orchestra, an insidious threat to her resistance, her senses already too highly charged from being in his arms.

That elusive scent of him, the warmth of his hand against her back, was far more pleasurable than she wanted to admit, and all the time her brain screamed his betrayal to her, causing her such unutterable anguish that she wondered how much more she could take before her heart burst.

When Colt eventually suggested that they go upstairs, she was more than glad to, if only to break that disturbing physical contact with him, but her pulse was racing madly as he unlocked the door to their suite. For God's sake, *tell* him! her brain urged riotously, but he was pulling her to him as he kicked the door closed, his mouth coming down on hers with a fierceness that assured her he couldn't wait for her any longer.

His heart thundered against hers, her own beating a frantic tattoo as her body threatened to yield to the hard, sensual demands of his. Suddenly, a strong instinct for survival was surfacing, and she was pulling forcibly away from him, shuddering as she saw the puzzlement in his face—the wounded question in his eyes.

'What's wrong?'

Raine cast her tongue over her dry lips, her breasts lifting sharply beneath the simple, black cocktail dress she had worn for dinner. 'I don't want you to,' she uttered in a voice that shook.

A deep furrow knitted Colt's brows. 'What do you mean . . . you don't want me to?' he asked heavily.

Raine swallowed hard, catching the faint aroma of red roses from a silver bowl on the coffee table; realised, with a hopeless surge of emotion that he must have ordered them for her when they had gone down to dinner, because they hadn't been there before. 'All right . . . I know I shouldn't have come away with you . . . let you think everything was all right . . . but I can't go through with it, Colt. I can't!' She was gabbling, not really sure what she was saying, her breath coming quickly as somehow, tremulously, she spat out, 'I'm not sleeping with a man who only married me for revenge!'

Puzzlement deepened in the strong face, and he was looking at her with his head at an angle, as if she had suddenly taken leave of her senses. 'What the hell are you talking about?'

She swallowed again, her heart thumping in her breast, tears very near the surface. 'I heard you . . . in the study this afternoon!' Her nails were digging into her palms, and it was all she could do to hold back the sobs which were threatening to choke her. 'Don't pretend you didn't say it, because I was coming downstairs and the door was open, and I heard you telling Tim that you only married me to get even with him! That you could gloat every time you . . . we . . .'

'You heard that?' His incredulous whisper brought her head

up sharply, and for one ridiculous moment she thought he was about to laugh. But his expression was changing to one of . . . bewilderment, she thought, puzzlingly, and guessed that it was probably from guilt at having been found out. 'What else did you hear?' he asked, frowning, and he spoke slowly, as if he were picking his words carefully.

'My God! Wasn't that enough?' Her hand going to her throat, she realised that he was openly admitting it, and she stared at him, disbelieving, feeling as if she'd been stabbed through the heart.

He moved towards her—tall and predatory in the dark dinner-jacket—and she couldn't understand the look of increasing bewilderment in his face as he saw her back instinctively away. 'For God's sake, Raine! Be sensible!' One hand shot out, catching her wrist, the other massaging the muscles at the nape of his neck. 'Do you really think I married you just for revenge?'

Pain twisted her insides as she had to admit to herself that he was much too shrewd and intellectual for that. 'Oh, no, I'm sure there were other very good reasons,' she breathed shudderingly, trying not to notice how the moonlight streamed in across the balcony, how erotically the breeze sang through the olive groves beyond the hotel. 'Like a resident bedmate, for one thing!' she accused bitterly, misery etched on her face. 'And a convenient new mother for Sean!'

Colt's eyes narrowed, anger flickering in their depths. 'I'll pretend I didn't hear that,' he breathed softly, his voice oddly controlled, while from outside came the churring song of a nightjar hunting insects on the warm, summer air. 'It was just unfortunate you came downstairs when you did . . .'

'Unfortunate?' Angrily, Raine pulled herself out of his grasp, hurting, wanting him to deny having said what he had—to lie to her, even. *Anything,* just to convince her that she had imagined what she had heard. But he wasn't denying it, and now the tears she had been struggling to keep at bay came

fast and freely. Through blurred vision she saw him make a
move towards her. 'Unfortunate for whom? Me? Or you?' she
threw at him, backing away, her sobs making it difficult for
her to breathe. 'You used me,' she uttered, miserably, cupping
her hands over her nose and mouth, 'just to hurt your brother.
God!' And now she looked at him hard, her teeth clenched,
unable to grasp the reason for the deepening query—the
darkening expression in his eyes. 'If you didn't have the
decency to consider my feelings in all this, I would have
thought you'd at least have been above wanting to hurt him!
Hasn't he paid enough already for what he did?'

'I see,' Colt breathed, his shoulders sagging as if something
had just become very apparent to him. He was but a few
inches away from her, and his mouth was set grimly as if he
were finding it a battle keeping his temper in check, though
she failed to see why. After all, *she* was the one who had been
hurt, wasn't she? 'What's really upsetting you, Raine?' He
surveyed her coldly, his head to one side. 'The fact that I
might just be the big, bad monster you want to think I am? Or
that I might just have gone out of my way to hurt your
precious Tim? Perhaps it's still Tim, eh?' His tone was as
chilling as ice. 'Because, talking of your feelings, what are they,
Raine? Why did you marry *me*? Since you're questioning *my*
motives, I don't seem to recall you once offering any
declarations of undying devotion to me.'

She couldn't, because she had been too unsure of him to
expose her emotions so entirely, especially since *he* hadn't,
although she'd hoped that with time she could make him
confide his love for her. What a stupid, naïve fool she'd been!
And now he was accusing her of still being in love with Tim!
Well, if he thought that, then she was prepared to let him, she
decided, torturedly, because she knew she'd never be able to
express her love openly to him now.

'Nothing to say?' The proud head tilted, his eyes assessing
her, his fingers splayed against the lean angle of his hips. 'If I

recall, you needed time to consider my proposal, so why the hell did you marry me? Because you were afraid I might have made you pregnant? Or simply for what I can do to you in bed?'

His words—the roughness of his voice—made her flinch. Why couldn't he understand why she was so upset? And why was he even querying her reasons for marrying him, she wondered grievously, when his own had been so cold and calculated? His last remark though, brought colour to her cheeks, and unhappily she reflected on how, until today, she'd been half hoping that she was pregnant with his child.

Swallowing back a fresh surge of emotion, she said pointedly, 'You don't really think I'd marry a man solely for sex, do you?' Her lips twisted disgustedly at the thought.

Behind them, the net curtains moved in the gentle breeze from the balcony, but inside the air was electric, and she saw Colt's mouth curl in a travesty of a smile.

'Oh, don't scoff at the idea, darling. It's a pretty powerful force. And you wouldn't be the first to do it, by any means.'

His comment generalised but, absently, Raine wondered if he was talking about Stephanie, although at that moment she was too upset to care. 'Well, I'm not one of them!' she was flinging back at him, her eyes glistening, her face blotchy from her tears. 'And if you think I'll let you touch me again after what you said to Tim today, you can think again, because I won't!'

For a moment, she thought he was going to say something. Staring down into her tear-streaked face—his, hard and expressionless—he seemed about to take a step towards her, but thought better of it. Then, his mouth tightening, suddenly he swung away from her across the room, and went out, slamming the door.

# CHAPTER EIGHT

THE honeymoon was over. As Colt pulled up outside the house, Sean was rushing down the steps ahead of his grandmother, and, climbing out of the car, Raine forced herself to smile as Ruth's lips brushed her cheek, although her pale countenance didn't escape her mother-in-law's shrewd eye.

'My dear, you're looking rather peaky.' She studied Raine gravely. 'You aren't sickening, are you?' She had been staying there, looking after her grandson for the three days they had been away—and obviously the garden as well, Raine realised, noticing every neatly pruned shrub. Furtively, she cast a glance towards Colt, who had scooped Sean up into his arms, his deep, warm laughter echoing the welcoming squeal of the child's.

'The flight was rather unsettling,' she bluffed, through that familiar tug of envy over the closeness between father and son. If only she could make him love her like that!

'You'd think I was the worst pilot in the world, wouldn't you, Mother?' he laughed, setting Sean down on his feet, and with a casual glance at Raine, 'You really must learn to trust your husband, darling.'

She wasn't sure what he meant—or why there had been a silent admonition behind his remark, because there had—but she knew he wasn't talking about his capability as a pilot. He flew a plane as he did everything—with absolute control and admirable skill. But, torturedly, she wondered how he could joke, and put on a remarkable show of being the contented bridegroom, when her own heart was breaking.

For the past three days there had been a cold war between

them, during which he hadn't attempted to touch her. Perhaps he was worried that, if he did, then she would leave him. And she had just cause to, she cogitated unhappily, watching him unload their cases from the car, although if he had called her bluff—tried to make love to her—she wasn't sure how she would have responded. But he hadn't, and they had walked through vineyards, tasted the wines of Provence, and sipped coffee under the coloured canopies of the street cafés like polite strangers, their conversation strained and awkward. Only once had they shared any physical contact, and that was when they were emerging from one rather ancient cathedral. Stepping out of the dark interior ahead of him into the dazzling sunlight, she had tripped over a step and he had caught her, the strength of his arm around her waist sending an electrifying sensation pulsing through her. Quickly, she had extricated herself from his disturbing proximity, refusing to acknowledge the fingers of need that tightened in the pit of her stomach. She had wanted him even then, she accepted, self-loathingly now, but to have let him see how much he could affect her without even trying would have been a humiliation she couldn't have borne. One day, she was sure, he would regret marrying her, and she knew she could only bear the consequences of that if he never knew how much she loved him. And if she were pregnant . . .

A fresh, northerly breeze came off the sea, tossing the conifers so that they looked like a line of uniform dancers with their hair in disarray, and she shivered, in spite of the sun. That was something she would have to accept if it transpired.

'I'm so glad you're back. Sean's been missing Colston terribly lately, and it will be so much better for him to be here . . . have someone here all the time, other than Mrs Bisson. It's what the boy needs.'

Mrs Bisson was a brusque, middle-aged woman of few words, and hardly the greatest of comforts for a motherless child, Raine had realised when she'd first met Colt's housekeeper. But she smiled wanly now at Ruth Falloner's concern, wondering uneasily what she would say if she knew that the marriage had been a disaster from the start—that already her stepson and his new bride were sleeping in separate rooms.

'Is Raine really going to stay here? All the time?' The little boy lifted eager blue eyes to his father. 'Will she be here *every* day?'

The entreaty in his voice tugged at Raine's heart, yet increased her own, personal anguish. It had been agreed during that brief engagement that she would give up her job and look after Sean—not least because she wanted to—but now she knew an immense stab of pain, remembering how desperately she had looked forward to fulfilling a mother's role in his life, to becoming Colt's wife . . .

'Isn't it natural for Mummies and Daddies to live together?' He had dropped down on to his haunches, level with his son, and was ruffling the little boy's hair. 'And I told you on Saturday . . . she's your new mother now, so you must remember to call her that . . . not Raine.' He straightened, giving Sean an affectionate tap on his backside, his voice gentle but firm as he recommended, 'Now, why don't you run over and give her a welcome like you gave me?'

Sean grinned shyly. Nibbled a forefinger. And then, to everyone's amusement, ran across and flung his arms tightly around Raine's waist. She gave a little burst of laughter, and wasn't sure whether it was simply his display of affection or his father's suggestion of it that brought a lump to her throat.

Hugging him to her, she looked up and met Colt's steady gaze—saw something there behind the smiling approval. A smugness. An awareness of the deep affection she already had for Sean, and absurdly she experienced the oddest sensation of a trap closing around her.

She wasn't pregnant. When she realised it, two days later, after seeing Ruth off, one half of her felt as if a huge cloud had suddenly been lifted, although she couldn't begin to explain the emotions the other half of her was enduring.

Getting ready to take Sean for an afternoon drive, she stood in front of the dressing-table mirror, twisting her hair into a top-knot, and was shocked at the look of empty resignation in the cool green eyes, the downcast line to the wide mouth. Had she really been hoping that she was carrying Colt's child? A man who had married her primarily to get even with the man who had dared to seduce his wife?

A wave of self-disgust washed over her, and she had to stifle a sob. Heavens, she knew the depth of his capacity for revenge! Hadn't she felt it directed at her initially? But did his need to avenge himself spring from a love he still felt for Stephanie? A bruised male ego? Or purely from Tim's disloyalty? Or all three? Whichever, it hurt to know that she, Raine, was simply an implement for that revenge, and with an immense effort of will she strove to bring her tears—the pain of loving him—under control, and went to look for Sean, though not before phoning the doctor's surgery to make an appointment.

They had talked, before the wedding, about starting a family immediately, but Raine knew she could never commit herself so completely now. And, although Colt still hadn't attempted to make love to her, she wondered just how long it would be before he insisted on claiming his marital rights. Also, she wasn't unaware of her own lack of immunity to that dangerous attracton of his, and so she wanted the surety of knowing that, if ever he did try to seduce her and she was foolish enough to succumb, at least she wouldn't become pregnant through her weakness. And that was surrender in itself, though she didn't realise it then, hiding her misery that afternoon behind a smile she wore for Sean; in fact, she found her smile came naturally after a while, because there was pleasure to be had in watching his face light up with delight as they walked around the island's nature reserve; basking in his unbridled excitement as the carp in the reed-fringed pond came up for the bread he had thrown in, left over from the sandwiches which Raine had made for them both.

They returned early in the evening, spending the hour after supper in a light-hearted game of snakes and ladders, and, when it was Sean's bed time, Raine gave in to his pleas to be read to, though she knew he could read remarkably well himself.

He was asleep before she closed the book, and she sat there for a while, taking comfort from the warmth of the small body through the duvet, loving him because he was part of Colt, the part that wasn't hardened or embittered by life—by love. Because it was love that had made him the way he was, she found some consolation in realising as she returned the adventure annual to Sean's bookcase. Love, disillusionment, hurt. She could remember only too clearly how wounded and embittered she'd been herself by Tim's unfaithfulness—someone she'd thought she'd loved, and trusted. And Colt was only behaving as he was now through the infidelity of the people *he'd* loved. If only there was some way that she could reach the real Colt, she thought wistfully, the man who worshipped Sean with a love that was heart-wrenching—the real man behind the rock-hard cynic. Even the painful suspicion that he might still be in love with Stephanie could be borne if she knew that, in time, she could make him love *her* . . .

Drawing Sean's floral curtains against the long, light evening, she wished she could blank out her ridiculous, fanciful hopes as easily. Downstairs, settling herself on the settee with her legs curled under her, she tried to involve herself in some reading of her own. It was a history book of Colt's, which normally she found very absorbing, but tonight her poor concentration wouldn't let her take in one page, and finally she snapped the book shut, just as she heard his key in the front door.

On impulse, she wanted to run and greet him; common sense and hurt feminine pride, however, wouldn't let her, and she was still curled up with the book on her lap when he came in.

A smile tugged at the hard mouth. 'Brushing up on your French aristocracy?' He was crossing the room with that easy grace of his, the light beige suit he was wearing somehow emphasising the rich lights in his hair, the hard bronze of his skin, and Raine tensed as he moved close enough to tilt the book so that he could read the author's name. 'He's got an easy style, hasn't he?'

'Yes.' To her dismay, it came out as a husky whisper, because he was standing too close to her—tall and very sophisticated, that familiar scent of him too disturbing to her senses.

'What have you done today?' She looked up at him, and felt her heartbeat quicken as her gaze locked with his.

'I took Sean to St Ouen's Pond.'

He seemed to be digesting this piece of information before his mouth curved in a smile. And suddenly he was bending, with one hand on the back of the settee, to kiss her, taking her so much by surprise that she didn't have time to even think about turning away.

It was the first intimate contact she'd had with him since their wedding night, and now repressed desire sent a treacherous warmth tingling through her blood, a twist of need so great in her loins that she pulled away from him in a rejection born of panic.

His eyes, as he straightened, narrowed to hard, crystal chips. 'Just how long are you going to deny yourself, darling?' His tone was nonchalant as he strode away from her, and, as if to emphasise how easy it was for him to do so, casually he stooped to pick up one of the daily newspapers that had been lying on the coffee table. Sitting down in the chair opposite her, he opened it and began whistling through his teeth.

Her heart still beating at twice its normal pace, Raine bit her lip to stop its trembling. He knew, of course, what he could do to her, and that discomfiting awareness of his—the knowledge of her own weakness for him—gave rise to sudden anger in her, so that she had to bite back the retort that was on the tip of her tongue. Retaliation would only show him how much he unsettled her, she decided, hopelessly.

She looked across at him, and said calmly instead, 'Sean wants a pond of his own. He's talked of nothing else all afternoon. I thought we could put it down by the magnolia tree, but I said I'd have to ask you first.'

There was surprise and something else—an almost injured look, she thought fancifully—in the rich clarity of his eyes. 'You're his mother now. This is your home. You don't have to ask for my *consent*,' he said half-angrily. 'Do anything you like.' And, flinging down his paper, he got up and walked out of the room, and a few moments later she heard him go upstairs.

She could have cried her frustration and despair. How could he expect her to assume the natural duties of a wife when she knew there was no love on his side for her? she wondered unhappily. And hurting, reluctant to face another evening of polite conversation and awkward silences, she went to check the casserole which Mrs Bisson had put in the oven before she'd left, laid the dining-table for one and, having no appetite herself, went upstairs to run a bath.

Climbing out half an hour or so later, soothed and more relaxed, she realised she had forgotten to bring in her robe, so she draped herself in a towel before starting back to her room.

She was half-way across the landing when the telephone started to ring. She had heard Colt go downstairs earlier, but he wasn't answering it, and when the ringing persisted she hurried along to the extension in the master bedroom. This was to have been *their* room, she couldn't help thinking, though only Colt was using it now, and she tried not to remember how they had both chosen the subtle autumn shades of the colour scheme to match the existing carpet and the light oak furniture. But she was aware of a needle-sharp pain somewhere around her heart as she picked up the phone.

It proved to be a wrong number and, as she dropped the receiver back on to its rest, clumsily she knocked some loose coins that had been lying beside it, and heard them drop down between the cabinet and the bed. She stooped to retrieve them, but one had rolled under the valance. And right to the other side! she realised with a grimace when she heard the soft clink as it hit one of the castors on the far side of the bed.

Scrambling across it, she reached underneath, finding the coin easily enough before pushing herself back up on to the bed. Her towel-clad body was a pale contrast against the darker silk of the duvet, and her pinned hair was coming loose, so that she couldn't even begin to guess how wanton and abandoned she looked moving sinuously across the bed. And suddenly, as she glanced up, a small gasp escaped her, her hand going instinctively to her throat as she met Colt's hard gaze in the doorway.

'Well . . . are you going to stay on top of it? Or do you think we'd be more comfortable under the sheets?'

He sounded amused, but angry, too. With her damp hair tumbling around her shoulders, Raine quickly clambered to her feet, the table-lamp she had switched on before answering the phone revealing the flame of colour that spread across her cheeks.

'I was taking a call,' she explained falteringly, her mind half registering that he had changed into a light, casual shirt and dark trousers.

'Like that?' His cursory glance over her semi-nakedness was heat-infusing. 'Draped across my bed?'

She could appreciate how odd that must seem to him and, in the circumstances, unwise, and she opened her hand to show him the coin she'd almost forgotten she was holding, placing it with the others beside the phone. His keys were there, too, she noticed now, guessing that he must have emptied his pockets in here before he'd changed.

'You weren't answering it,' she said, her heart fluttering in her breast, because he had crossed the room and, intentionally or not, was barring her escape. The cabinet was preventing her from stepping aside and, if she'd taken a step back, she knew she would probably have fallen back on the bed again, so she stayed exactly where she was.

'I was looking at where you wanted the pond before it was too dark,' Colt said then, appearing as composed as she was otherwise. 'You made a good choice.' Approval lit his eyes. 'And you picked up the extension just as I went to pick up the phone in the hall. Was it anything important?'

His disturbing nearness made her too aware of how little she was wearing, and she shook her head, her mouth too dry for her to speak. Absently, she heard the hall clock chime the hour. He moved closer to her, ignoring her panicky, 'Colt, please . . .' as he reached for her, his hands sliding gently over the pale slope of her shoulders, moving with subtle intimacy along the length of her arms.

'I know. You don't want me to.' She heard his husky comment through heady panic, every nerve in her body leaping in betraying response to his touch. 'Do you know . . . you were wearing a towel the first time I kissed you?' He merely smiled at the warning she flashed him, holding her there so that his eyes could make their lazy appraisal of her body. 'I'll never know how I restrained the urge to rip it off you that night,' he breathed, his eyes suddenly darkening. It was that transmitted message that threw her senses into chaos, and brought her hands up against the hard wall of his chest in self-protection and alarm. 'Now there's no need for restraint, is there, Raine?'

She tried to twist away from him, and with a small cry came up against the solid strength of his arm, sensations ripping through her as she felt the coolness of his sleeve against her bare midriff, and realised to her horror that the towel was now lying in a creamy pool around her feet.

'Your own doing, darling . . . not mine.' There was amusement in the dry tones, appreciation in the hot gaze flicking
over her nakedness and, mortified, she realised that he was
right. He hadn't actually touched the towel; it had been her
own efforts to resist him that had loosened it. She stood rigid
in the circle of his arms, trembling as he dipped his head to
kiss the sensitive skin of her shoulder, her throat, the delicate
shell of her ear. The touch of his lips was so feather-like that
unbidden responses leaped through her, making her body ache
with need. Under her fingers she could feel the hard
drumming of his heart and, half aware, she heard the sounds of
a summer evening: cattle lowing in the pasture on the
adjoining farm, the chirping of crickets and, attracted by the
lamp, the soft tapping of a moth against the window.

'Don't,' she whispered raggedly, when he transferred the
sweet torment of his kisses to her other shoulder, but he paid
no attention to her protest and, with one hand against the
small of her back, was suddenly easing her down on to the bed.

Every nerve awakened as his weight came down on hers, the
cool, smooth cotton of his clothes unbearably sensual against
the fevered heat of her skin.

'You want me to leave you alone . . . deny I want you?' he
breathed hoarsely, feathering kisses from her throat to the
deep, scented valley of her breasts. 'I can't.' He half groaned
his weakness, his need of her. 'Because I do want you, Raine
. . . very much.' His voice trembled with desire, making her
realise how close he was to losing control.

She had to stop him! she thought, reasoning wildly. But he
was too strong to push away, and her small sob of protest was
suddenly being silenced by the firm pressure of his mouth.
And he must have known what devastating effects that would
have, because suddenly she was kissing him back, her hands
desperately seeking the hard muscle of his shoulders, clutching
him to her, her body arching for even greater contact, her head

tipping back to allow his kiss to deepen.

She thought she would drown beneath the warm strength of him, in the scent of his aftershave that still clung to his unshaven jaw. And somewhere at her shoulder she could hear his wristwatch, ticking in unison with the frantic beating of her heart.

She gave a throaty sob as his fingers trailed across her too eagerly responding breasts, his lips following where his hands had been, his touch so infinitely tender that she gave another small moan.

'What is it, Raine?' His voice was a warm caress. 'What do you want?' He looked up at her, his strong profile flushed with passion. Yet, strangely, he looked as vulnerable as she felt, she thought wonderingly. And she knew, in that moment, that she wanted him to take her, to ignore her protests and take the matter into his own hands—anything, to know the ecstasy of his lovemaking again. But he seemed to read her mind and said gently, 'No. When you give yourself to me, I want it to be because your mind wants it, too . . . not just your body. And that means sorting out this ridiculous state of affairs between us.'

His words tugged her out of her sensual daze and back to reality with cruel effectiveness. He was more in control than she'd realised, while she was still breathless and trembling from her arousal. She looked at him where he lay, to one side of her now, his head resting on his hand, gazing down at her. Inwardly, she shuddered, wondering exactly how he proposed to 'sort it out'. How did he intend justifying marrying her for revenge? she thought bitterly, turning away from him. And, drawing her knees up so that her body wasn't so exposed to him, she murmured fixedly to the duvet, 'I don't want to talk about it.'

His sharp breath was drawn in anger, but it was gentle pressure he used to turn her half back to him, the touch of his hand on her bare shoulder sending new desire through her in spite of herself.

'We're going to have to talk about it,' he stated coolly, his dark gaze flickering over the tense lines of her face, the soft curvature of her forehead, her desire-flushed cheeks, and the wounded, obstinate thrust of her lower lip. 'If you'd just come to your senses . . . stop acting like a stubborn, petulant child, you'd . . .'

A small cry from the other room stopped him in mid-sentence. Sean was sobbing for him—waking from a bad dream—although Colt didn't move immediately. He was still looking down at her, his eyes intent, so warm and reflective as they held hers that she had the sudden, desperate longing to turn into him, to pour out her heart and accept the ultimate humiliation of his knowing how much she loved him. But she couldn't face that. Anyway, Sean was still crying.

She tugged away from Colt, rising to see to the little boy herself, but gently he pressed her back and got up and, seeing her shiver, lifted the duvet up around her.

'One day, darling, you're going to have to ask yourself why the hell you married me,' he breathed, with a quiet harshness which was totally at variance with the gentleness of his last action. And he went out, leaving Raine sobbing silently into the duvet, wondering again how he could even dare to question *her* motives.

Over the next few days she saw very little of him. When he wasn't at the office, he was away, conducting business in England, or spending a lot of his time organising the running of the farm. With the latter, Raine knew she could have enjoyed helping him, but it became apparent almost immediately that their personal problems were making even working together a strain, and so she spent most of her time alone, or with Sean, at the house.

Arranging contractors for the pond the day after she'd agreed it with Colt, she remembered what he'd said about the place being her home—that she could do what she liked. So, shaking herself out of her despondency, she found herself ready to admit that there were things she wanted to do to make the place cosier. That very afternoon she began making mental notes of the things she wanted to buy: plants, the odd lamp for a rather dark corner, new cushions and curtains. And for the next few days she almost forgot how unhappy she was, losing her worries in a hectic spree—matching colours, designs, soft furnishings—so that even Colette was fooled by her temporary high spirits, remarking upon them when they met for a snack one lunch time.

'I see marriage agrees with you,' she enthused at once, noticing Raine's healthy flush, brought on purely from rushing around the shops. 'Cloud nine hasn't burst yet then, Raindrop, and brought you tumbling down?'

Raine rolled her eyes and groaned laughingly at the double pun. If only Colette knew!

'Did you expect it to?' she attempted lightly, determined to hide the problems of her marriage from Colette at any cost. They were too personal to share with anyone.

Colette shrugged, cornflower-blue eyes emphasised by a dress of the same shade. 'I suppose I'm just a bit dubious about marriage still,' she admitted above the café sounds: the hiss of an Espresso machine, the clink of crockery, the babble of mixed conversations. She pulled a wry face. 'Still, I've done it now, Raine . . . told Dave I'll marry him, only it won't be for a year or so yet.'

Raine glanced up from buttering a toasted teacake, gaping with surprise. 'Congratulations!' she expressed, her face lighting up. But Colette wasn't allowing herself to get excited.

'Sometimes I wish he'd do what Colt did to you . . . just whisk me off and get it over with,' she remarked wistfully. 'Then I wouldn't have time to get cold feet.' She pulled a self-deprecating smile. 'Isn't that cowardly? Still, I'm glad everything's working out all right for you.'

A gossamer line knitted Raine's brows. She felt dreadful,

deceiving her friend like this. Even by saying nothing she knew she was misleading Colette, and she was glad when the other girl changed the subject, curious to see what Raine had been buying, her eyes trained on the numerous bags on the seat beside her friend.

Raine showed her. There was curtain material. Several attractively designed plant-pots to house the plants she'd bought earlier in the week. A small, original water-colour of Gorey—a fishing village on the island's east coast—and a remote-controlled, little silver saloon for Sean.

'What does the lord and master think of this sudden whim to improve the love-nest?' Colette asked laughingly, her very inaccurate description of Raine's new home sending a sharp pain through her. But she smiled in spite of it. Colt's initial reaction when he'd come home that first night and seen all the new furnishings dotted around the place had been one of surprise, and then approval, evident from the smile that had tugged at the corners of his mouth. She'd been standing on a chair, clad in tight jeans and a clinging summer top, hanging a painting, very much aware of Colt's eyes on her, before he'd drawled softly, 'So you have taste, too.' Crazily, she had blushed. But he *had* approved, and she conveyed as much to Colette, her eyes shining with the warmth she still felt at having pleased him.

The blue eyes studied her, dark head at an angle. 'You love him very much, don't you?'

Stupidly, she felt a rush of tears—a pressure on her windpipe —and she nodded, too overcome to speak. Yes, she did, she thought. Too much. And knew she could only cope with that just as long as Colt never found out.

Leaving Colette, she finished her shopping and collected Sean from his new school, driving him to a playmate's birthday party where, since it was Saturday the following day, it had been agreed that he would spend the night. When, outside his friend's door, Raine handed him the little car she'd bought, his eyes sparkled with delight.

'It's the same as Daddy's!' he grinned triumphantly, and Raine kissed him, touched by Sean's obvious pride in his father.

'Yes, like Daddy's,' she whispered, her throat constricting, and, watching him go inside with his new toy tucked proudly under his arm, she knew she couldn't have loved him more if he had been her own child.

Back home, she put the finishing touches to the new living-room curtains and hung them, standing back to admire the effect the soft, rose colour created in the room. It added warmth, unlike the colourless cream of the ones that had been hanging there before and, pleased with her efforts, she sat down then to write a short letter to her parents, knowing that they would expect one by now. She kept her news brief, giving them no hint of her problems, simply letting them know that she was settling in. And afterwards, on a sudden crazy impulse to hear Colt's voice, she telephoned the marina, ostensibly to ask him what time he would be home.

'I'm afraid Colt's been at a meeting with Miss Day since lunch time, and he said he wouldn't be back until late.' Sheila's reply came unwelcomingly to Raine. 'Can I take a message?'

There was none and, thanking her, Raine replaced the receiver, experiencing a stab of some ridiculous emotion. So Jocelyn Day was back on the island. And, if her usual attitude towards Colt was anything to go by, Raine bet her life that the other woman wouldn't let the discussions rest solely with business. She knew she was being foolish, but she couldn't help the jealousy which gnawed at her. After all, Colt was a healthy, virile man, and she hadn't exactly been too generous with her conjugal favours. And he was going to be late.

Shaking such unpleasant thinking aside before it took too firm a hold, she decided to jog it off, and changing hurriedly into shorts and light top, went for a long run to the farm and back, fixing herself a snack as soon as she returned, and then going up to take a shower.

She had scarcely undressed when she heard a car pulling up outside, and her heart missed a beat. Colt! If it was, then he'd forgotten his key, she realised a few moments later, when the doorbell rang.

There was no one else in, since Mrs Bisson had left for the day, so, flinging on a creamy satin negligee, Raine went down to open the door.

Timothy stood there, leaning heavily on his stick, the evening shadows in the porch emphasising the scar on his cheek, making him look almost sinister.

'Well . . .' he drawled, the smile which spread across his face making Raine uncomfortably aware that he knew she was naked beneath her wrap. 'Am I interrupting something . . . personal? Or does my brother like you like this to whet his appetite before bed time?'

Piqued, Raine glared at him, wishing it was anyone but Tim. 'What do you want?' she demanded, her eyes wary.

Timothy clicked his tongue disapprovingly, raking back his straight, blond hair. 'That isn't exactly a friendly greeting for your new brother-in-law, is it?' he commented, with a grimace. 'As a matter of fact, I seem to have missed out on getting to kiss the bride.'

'Don't you dare!' Her hands flew up to push at him as he would have kissed her, but instead he was dodging round her, admitting himself into the hall.

One glance took in the new plants and paintings, the soft, evening sunlight—pink-tinged—filtering out from the lounge, and his mouth pulled in wry approval. 'Where's Colt?'

Beneath that usual display of arrogance, she sensed that he seemed nervous, and her breast lifted as she felt herself tense up. 'He's not here.' She said it automatically, then wished she hadn't when she saw the surprise and then the sudden gleam that lit his eyes. Or was it relief? she wondered, realising that he'd been drinking as she smelt the alcohol on his breath.

'Oh?' There was a wealth of understanding in that one syllable. 'Working late already? That isn't very fair on his new bride.' He looked at her obliquely—less sinister in the still-sunny hall. In fact, he would probably attract a lot of women even now, she thought, dispassionately, before he said, 'It's just as well I called round, isn't it?'

Raine stood her ground as he came closer, concealing her discomfiture behind a cool, 'No, it isn't. And if you don't mind, Tim, I'd appreciate it if you'd just leave.'

He shrugged, limping in an ungainly fashion to the door, and Raine breathed relief, which turned instantly to apprehension, when she saw him use his stick to push it closed.

'What are you doing?' Colour heightened on her cheekbones, and she knew a small trickle of fear as he came back to her.

'What time will Colt be home?'

Raine swallowed, edging away from him, and was brought up sharply by the hard wood of the door-jamb against her back. 'Soon,' she bluffed, having no idea when Colt was likely to return.

Timothy studied her standing in a stream of pink light, his gaze raking over the gentle tumble of curls and the feminine curves beneath her wrap, lifting again to the pale ivory of her face, the clouded misery in her eyes. He said quietly, 'You're a liar. You don't know what time he's coming home, do you?' Fair brows drew together, and he was whispering incredulously, 'Aren't things working out?'

She'd forgotten how shrewd he was. But then, he was Colt's half-brother, she reminded herself, so it wasn't surprising that they should share one characteristic.

'You'd like to think so, wouldn't you?' she accused bitterly, unconsciously gripping the door-jamb for support. After all, he was the one person who knew the real reason for Colt's marrying her, and she guessed that it would probably satisfy Tim's ego immensely to know that his brother's second marriage was a farce as well.

'No, Raine. I want to see you happy.'

She was so taken aback by his seemingly sincere concern that, when he caught her elbow to lead her into the living-room, she didn't resist.

'We have to talk,' he stressed, turning her to face him in front of the huge, white marble fireplace. 'You wouldn't see me after . . . it happened,' he said hesitantly, and Raine flinched, knowing he was referring to the accident—their break-up. 'Colt thinks I was coming here that night to pour out my troubles to him,' Tim went on, his voice suddenly hoarse, 'but I knew he was in England. I was coming to see Stephanie, drunk as I was, to tell her it was all over between her and me. I'd already telephoned her to say I was on my way.' He glanced up, staring at the new rose-coloured curtains as if he wasn't really seeing them, his features oddly contorted. 'I think she knew why I was driving over, because she got upset and wanted to come to my flat instead . . . probably to try and talk me out of ending the affair. I think that was where she was headed when I swung in and hit her car that night. But I never wanted that to happen—any of it!' With a deep, agonised groan, he dropped his face into his hands, his stick hanging limply from his fingers. Surprised by his sudden outburst, Raine bit her lip, feeling a surge of pity for him. Tentatively, she put out a hand, then, thinking better of it, let it fall again.

'I didn't want to know at first,' Timothy continued, dragging his fingers down the flawed, handsome face, 'but God! she was so persuasive! Any man would have cracked under the strain . . . although I wouldn't expect Colt to understand that.' Raine jumped as his stick hit one of the soft, leather chairs, the sound splitting the air. 'He's got a will of iron.' His features were twisted in ugly lines as he went on, 'She didn't really prefer me to Colt.' His tone was self-derisive—as though even the possibility of it were laughable. 'Any man would have done. Colt would have needed to have been a super stud to have satisfied her. She was sick, Raine! And I fell for it . . . ruined things for us and loused up Colt's life . . .' He broke off, his voice cracking, turning his face sharply away from her.

Unbelievably, he was crying, eaten up with remorse over what he had done. And this time, overcome with pity, Raine couldn't prevent herself from reaching out to him, her fingers a light touch on his sleeve.

As if that small gesture from her was all he needed, he was pulling her into his arms, burying his face in the softness of her hair, his body shaken by hard, uncontrollable sobs.

He was like a child, she thought—weak and vulnerable—wondering in that moment whatever had attracted her to him in the first place. But pityingly her heart went out to him and, without conscious thought, her arms were around him and she was stroking his hair as she did sometimes with Sean when he was upset. But it was Colt she couldn't help sympathising with as she stood there comforting his brother.

So it had been a sickness with Stephanie, she reflected, her heart torn by the misery she knew he must have suffered because of it—hurting so much for him that at that moment she'd almost forgotten about Tim.

Standing there in the soft, evening sunlight, she felt his body stiffen, and knew why, the instant he pulled sharply away from her.

'What the . . .' Colt was in the doorway, his eyes blazing, his face as dark as thunder. 'Get out of here,' he snarled, his fists clenched at his sides as he came towards his brother. 'Get out of here, Tim, or so help me, I'll break every bone in your body!'

Timothy's face was white with shock. And probably fear, too, Raine realised, shuddering, because Colt looked murderous. But Timothy wasn't staying around to see if he would carry out his threat.

With one stumbling movement, he grabbed the stick he had

inadvertently dropped, and with remarkable speed got out of his brother's way. Raine's blood seemed to coagulate as she heard the front door slam hard behind him, leaving her alone with Colt.

'What the hell was he doing here?' he growled, his chest lifting heavily beneath the white silk shirt. 'Was that why you rang me?' His eyes were hard, grim. 'Oh, yes . . . Sheila left a message on her pad,' he interposed, explaining away her silent query as to how he had found out. 'What were you doing? Checking up what time I'd be home so that you could ask your lover over in the meantime?'

His face was flushed with anger, his eyes accusing, producing a retaliatory emotion in Raine. 'Don't be ridiculous!' Bright spots of colour were deepening on her cheekbones, and absently she realised that she didn't know why Tim had called. 'I didn't invite him here.'

'But you went willingly into his arms!' His accusations hurt, and it disgusted her that he could even think it about her. She swept away from him, running upstairs to get away from his pulsing anger, her stomach churning sickeningly when she heard his hard footsteps behind her. 'Oh, no, you don't!' At her bedroom door, he caught her arm, pulling her round to face him, his features a taut mask as he stared down into the indignant beauty of hers. 'I want an explanation for that little scene down there, and I want it now!'

Her eyes flashed angrily in defiance of his command. 'I don't owe you anything, Colt,' she said, surprisingly coolly, pulling away. 'And if I did try to explain, you wouldn't believe me. You're so eaten up with wanting to get even with Tim, all you care about is hurting him, and me in the process!' She had crossed the room, flung open a drawer, and was going through the motions of selecting clean underwear for after her shower. 'Do you really think I'd have married you if I'd wanted an affair with *him?*'

'Why not?' His tone was laced with cold scepticism as he

moved across to her. 'I've learned the hard way never to trust a woman's motives!'

*'But I'm not Stephanie!'* She hurled it at him as she swung to face him, the hard sparkle in her eyes contesting with the glittering amber of his. And yet, there was a pained look about him that seemed to wrench her heart as she thought how glad she was that Sean was out of the house, so that he couldn't hear them shouting at each other. 'God, Colt, what sort of opinion . . .' She broke off as his fingers clamped around her wrist, preventing her from closing the drawer, and her heart came up into her mouth as his other hand curled over the self-evident little card that had been lying carelessly among her lingerie.

'My wife has asked me not to touch her, and yet she's taking the contraceptive pill?'

What was in his mind was obvious from the harsh contortion of his features, and she could only admit despairingly to herself how things must look.

'There were reasons,' she murmured, her voice suddenly meek, and she touched her tongue to her top lip, knowing that she could never explain them to him.

A tawny eyebrow lifted, and a muscle tugged in his jaw. 'What sort of reasons, Raine?' His voice dangerously low, he made a move towards her and, clutching her clothes to her breast, instinctively she backed away. But what could she say? *I want you so much that if you try to make love to me I won't be able to stop you, and I wanted to be safe?* How could she tell him that?

And suddenly her temper snapped from her frustration with the whole situation, the futile wanting, and the desperate, hopeless longing for his love. And, wanting to hurt him as much as she was hurting inside, recklessly she was flinging at him, 'What's wrong, Colt?' Her eyes were wounded and dark. 'Can't you take the thought of losing two wives to the same man?'

As soon as she saw the way the blood drained out of his face, she wished she hadn't said it, but it was too late. Appalled at herself, she tried to dart out of his way, and let out a small cry as he caught her, his fingers biting painfully into her soft flesh as they fastened hard around her upper arms.

'You little . . .'

Slut, she thought he called her, his breathing and his words so torn from him that it was lost in the fierce heat of his emotion. And then she was being flung from him, backwards, down on to the yielding softness of the bed. Her 'Colt, no!' was an anguished appeal to him as he loomed above her, his expression unrelenting, his breathing hard and controlled.

She stared up at him, trembling and breathless, knowing, from the hard rising of his chest—the taut muscles of his face—that if he gave vent to his anger now it would be in the most humiliating way. And how close he came to it, she didn't know, because, amazingly, some shred of that tremendous control had him swinging away from her, and a few moments later she heard a door slam, and then his car pulling away.

# CHAPTER NINE

RAINE woke the next morning with a throbbing head and, after getting up, discovered that Colt hadn't come home. His bed hadn't been slept in, she realised, when she passed his bedroom door; unhappily, she wondered where he had stayed. With Jocelyn Day? She couldn't bear the thought of that, and it was no consolation to accept that, if he had, then she had probably driven him to it. True, he hadn't married her for love, she mused sadly, staring at the too pale reflection that met her in the bathroom mirror. But in spite of that he had always treated her with respect, and she knew that, at the very least, she owed him some measure of respect in return. The pain in his face when she had flung those cruel and inane words at him would be stamped on her memory for life, and even if it had been only wounded masculine pride, then she was intelligent enough to realise that the wound had been immense.

Whatever had made her say such a thing? she wondered, hating herself. To taunt him with such a cruel, deliberate gibe? Well, whatever had provoked it, she thought, going over the bitter events of their quarrel as she had for one long, almost sleepless night, it had been unforgivable.

Mechanically, she dressed, pulling on jeans and a sweater since the morning was chill, and went downstairs to make herself a cup of coffee. Then, missing Sean, she was just about to telephone his friend's mother to ask if he was ready to be picked up, when she heard the front door opening. She turned, every muscle and nerve tensing itself for this dreaded confrontation, when she saw Sean run in ahead of his father.

156

'Mummy!'

The patter of tiny feet brought him into her arms, and Raine hugged him tightly before Colt's sharp, 'Sean!' came to them across the hall. The little boy turned bewildered eyes towards his father, clearly unable to understand the reason behind his razor-edged tone. And, without moving from the door, Colt said more gently, 'I believe the workmen finished your pond yesterday. Why don't you go out and take a look at it?'

Sean gave an excited gasp. 'And you, Mummy?' Already he was tugging at her hand.

'No. Mummy's staying here.' The cutting way in which he emphasised her title assured her of just how unfit he thought she was to bear it. As Sean ran off, oblivious to the animosity between his father and his new wife, they faced each other without speaking.

The light coming in from a window was storm-grey, slashing lines across Colt's face. His hair was windblown and his eyes—dark with disdain—held hers, which were lucid with a silent appeal to him, which turned out to be futile when he brushed past her and started upstairs.

'Colt, wait!' She couldn't bear it—this cold, chilling attitude towards her, this old contempt in him, which was a thousand times worse to accept now because she loved him so much. Pain seemed to twist her insides and she was running after him. 'Colt, wait, please! We have to talk!'

'I don't think so.' The negative words were thrown down to her without him even bothering to turn around.

'Colt . . . please.' She was desperate now. Prepared to do or say anything to earn back his respect. Breathlessly, she followed him into his bedroom. He had shrugged out of the casual jacket and was taking a clean shirt out of a drawer.

Raine swallowed hard. 'I'm sorry,' was all she could manage in a small, tremulous voice.

He shot her a hard look as he thrust the drawer shut, one eyebrow lifting scornfully. 'For what?' His tone was abrasive.

'Being the second Mrs Falloner to play the whore with my brother?'

His lashing response made her wince, though not half as much as the emotion she couldn't make out behind those words. She watched him go into the adjoining bathroom, her delicate features paler than usual against the striking contrast of auburn hair.

'It wasn't like that!' she threw after him, and, when he didn't answer, moved over to the bathroom door. He was taking off his shirt, his back to her. Shakily, she murmured, 'Colt . . . I haven't slept with Tim.'

He swung round, his bronze chest bared, and a prickly feeling ran down her spine from remembering how it felt to run her fingers over that coarse triangle of hair. Dark amber spheres bored into hers as he supplied, unrelentingly, 'But you intended to.'

Of course. The pills he'd discovered.

She was no more inclined now than she'd been the previous night to let him know how vulnerable her feelings were where he was concerned, but she was past lying to him and, with a small flutter in her stomach, she uttered flatly, 'No.'

He was tugging on a short-sleeved white shirt, but her admission stalled him in the act, his gaze intense as it noted the flush high on her cheekbones, the throbbing little pulse at the base of her throat. For the first time she noticed the dark shadows under his eyes, how strained he looked, and had the oddest impression that he shuddered.

'So,' he reasoned, and with his hands on his hips came towards her, his shirt gaping to the waist. 'I'm being admitted to your bed, as long as I don't contaminate that lovely body by impregnating you, is that it?'

She couldn't look at him, hurt by the acerbity in his voice when she had expected . . . what? Tenderness because of her admission? She didn't know, but her heart was screaming, *I'd have as many babies as you wanted if you'd only tell me you love me!*

He caught her small chin, tilting her flushed face to the hard maturity of his, and she shut her eyes, afraid of the emotion she could feel overwhelming her, afraid that he would recognise it with the questing sagacity which darkened his. With her eyes closed, she was still too aware of him. Of his nearness. His familiar scent. And for a moment she almost imagined that that strong hand trembled. But then, suddenly, the telephone started ringing.

She didn't even have to look at him to know that he was disinclined to answer it, but after a moment he strode around the bed to pick it up.

It was someone from the office, she realised, hearing his clipped replies, and knew that, even though it was Saturday, there would still be a skeleton staff on duty.

'I have to go out,' he said, coming back to her, fastening his shirt. 'But you're right,' there was an odd inflexion in his voice, 'we have to talk,' although he made it quite apparent that he didn't intend to then, because he picked up his jacket and strode out, leaving Raine feeling even more miserable than she had before.

Trying to take her mind off things, she went outside to find Sean, thinking some air and a game of frisbee might make her feel better. But the wind was too rough, and the violence of the sea in the bay made her shudder, so that after a few moments she retrieved the frisbee and hustled Sean inside.

The phone was ringing again when she reached the hall and, answering it, was alarmed to hear Ruth asking rather anxiously for Colt.

Her anguished groan, when Raine told her he wasn't in, prompted her daughter-in-law to ask, 'Is anything wrong?'

'Yes,' Ruth responded, and Raine's stomach turned over, her mind imagining all sorts of things. 'Timothy phoned me last night and asked me to come over,' Ruth explained hastily. 'He sounded near to breaking point.' There was a pause, as though she were hesitant to go on. And then she said, 'I may as well tell you, Raine . . . Timothy came over to the mainland a week or so ago, and we thrashed out a few home-truths. I tried to make him see the wrongfulness of what he'd done with Stephanie—that it wasn't helping anyone carrying on with this pointless jealousy and animosity towards his brother. I thought I was wasting my breath, but I think it must have done some good, because he said he called round last night to see Colston to try and make amends, but that he wasn't in. He said he was hoping that he could get *you* to convince his brother how dreadful he feels, when Colston came in and got the wrong idea about the two of you being together, and practically threw Timothy out.' Heat suffused Raine's cheeks from remembering the bitter argument that had ensued, but at least now she knew why Tim had called, what had been behind that surprising and complete change in him last night—Ruth! And now she realised why he'd looked relieved when she'd said she was alone. Offering his apologies through her had probably seemed far less daunting to him than apologising to Colt direct. But wasn't that like Tim, she accepted silently—almost regretfully at having to think it—to take the easy way out?

'He said he couldn't stand how unforgiving Colston's being,' she heard the other woman say, 'and I really think guilt's worn him down, Raine. And at the risk of sounding like the biased mother . . .' there was self-deprecation in Ruth's voice '. . . I think that's been the problem all along . . . why he's behaved the way he has since the accident—guilt.'

Mentally, Raine had to agree. And she knew that her mother-in-law wasn't trying to make excuses for Tim. Sadly, she realised that Ruth was only too aware of her son's shortcomings for that.

'Anyway,' she was continuing, 'I've flown over this morning and let myself in, but there's no sign of Timothy, and I've got this awful feeling that he might be going to do something stupid.'

Absently nodding to the middle-aged woman who had just come in, Raine turned away, hugging her free arm. 'What do you mean?' she asked worriedly, recovering from her surprise at realising that Ruth was on the island. 'What makes you think that?'

'You didn't hear how he sounded last night.' His mother's brief statement made Raine's brow crease. Tim had been in a pitiful enough state when he'd called on her and, if he was that disturbed by what he'd done, then Colt couldn't have helped matters coming in the way he had last night and threatening him, even though she could understand how things must have looked. 'There's a glass, and a half-empty bottle of whisky on the dining-table,' Ruth went on, her concern for her son apparent in her voice, 'so it's obvious he's been drinking. And I had a word with his landlady just now, and she said she saw him drive off about half an hour ago, towing his dinghy!'

'What?' Clutching the receiver with both hands, Raine swung to face the window. The wind was creating havoc with the trees in the drive, and even indoors she could hear how forcefully the sea was crashing into the bay. Tim was an experienced sailor, but there would be little chance for a small dinghy out there in this weather.

An icy fear gripped her. Perhaps, in his troubled state, that was what he was hoping, she thought, shuddering.

'We've got to get hold of Colston.' Ruth's urgent declaration cut through Raine's chilling thoughts. 'Where is he likely to be? At the farm?'

'No, he—he's at the office,' she remembered, raking her fingers agitatedly through her windswept hair. Despite her own problems she knew that she should offer to contact him herself. Ruth was obviously distraught, and Raine couldn't let her handle this alone. 'Don't worry . . . I'll get in touch with him,' she assured Ruth consolingly, although her stomach muscles clenched painfully a few moments later when she dialled his office number.

'Colt! It's Tim . . .' she began on hearing his deep acknowledgment, and with dismay realised that, after what he'd seen last night, he'd probably read more into her concern for his brother than there actually was. But she was as worried about Tim as Ruth was, and she knew there was no time for preliminaries. Briefly, she explained about Tim's telephone call to his mother—the reason for it—catching her breath mid-sentence because Colt wasn't saying a word, the tense silence at the other end of the phone so palpable she could almost touch it. 'Ruth thinks he might be drunk . . . and she said the neighbours saw him taking the boat out—'

'In *this*?' The incredulity behind Colt's sharp exclamation assured her of what she already knew. Any sailor would be half crazy to attempt to sail in weather like this. 'Bloody stupid idiot! How long ago did he go out?'

Anxiously, Raine put a hand to her temple. Then remembered what Ruth had told her. 'About half an hour ago,' she answered, and heard her husband swear again under his breath. 'Colt . . .' she began, tentatively then, her stomach churning. 'What you saw last night . . . wasn't anything. Tim was sorry . . . upset about what he'd done. He was actually cry—'

'Have you called the coastguard?' His hard interruption told her he had no wish to discuss the previous night, and Raine flinched, feeling as though she had been slapped. So he still hadn't forgiven her?

'No,' she uttered, feeling sick inside, and wanting to kick herself for not thinking of calling the coastguard herself. 'I wanted to ask your advice first.'

'Then ring him now.' He was suddenly in charge—taking over. 'I'll handle things from here.'

Raine's mouth went dry. 'What are you going to do?'

'Go after him. Isn't that what you want?'

His terse, clipped response confirmed her deepest fears, and she ignored the accusation in his question, her knuckles showing white where she gripped the receiver so tightly. 'No, Colt!'

But the line had gone dead. Despairingly, Raine knew that she couldn't have stopped him even if she had tried. Tim was his brother, no matter what he had done, and instinctively she knew that Colt wouldn't have stood by and left the rescue solely to the lifeboat had it been anyone he knew out there. His own cruiser, the *Cassandra,* was moored in the marina, so he would probably take that, she assumed. And Tim would probably have started out from the next bay, since that was the one nearest his flat, so Colt might not have too far to look for his brother. Even so, she couldn't help feeling afraid. Colt was an extremely proficient seaman, but there were treacherous rocks to negotiate, as well as the wind and the fury of the sea today, and the currents around the Channel Islands could be deadly, even in the best of weather. Raine paled, her brow furrowing with worry. Supposing something happened to him . . .

The thought made her cold with fear, and she shook it away, pulling herself together. Colt had asked her to ring the coastguard, and she did so now without further hesitancy, explaining about Tim and telling the man of Colt's rescue attempt from the marina, after which she telephoned Ruth to tell her mother-in-law what was happening. Then, knowing that she couldn't just sit around and wait, Raine went in search of Sean and Mrs Bisson, finding them both in the kitchen and explaining that she had to go out for a while. Flinging an anorak over her sweater and jeans, she set off for the marina, hoping that, if Colt found Tim and everything was all right, that he would naturally bring the *Cassandra* back there.

The wind tore at her face as she got out of the Fiat and crossed the car park of Island Marine, sudden gusts tossing the boats at their moorings, the creak of wood and lash of waves against the harbour wall making her all too conscious of the sea's menacing strength against man's. And Colt was out there somewhere . . .

She tried not to imagine in what situation he might be at that moment, her gaze unwittingly going to the bleak horizon. The dark, forbidding sea was being whipped into a white frenzy by the gale, and a thickening mist was coming down over the headland.

In a moment of weakness, Raine felt the strongest urge to cry. She had wanted to tell him again over the phone that she was sorry for what she'd said last night, even though she had done it out of a hopeless desperation for his love. But he hadn't been in a mood to listen, which was probably all her own fault, she realised miserably, and knew that, if anything happened to him out there, she would never forgive herself.

Fighting back tears, she went into the building and told the security guard in reception who she was, that she was expecting Mr Falloner back shortly and that she'd like to wait in his office. The man acquiesced at once, obviously delighted to be of assistance to the managing director's wife, even bringing her a cup of coffee and chatting for a few moments before going back to his duties.

After he'd gone, Raine finished the hot beverage and stood staring out of the window, shivering as she watched the turbulent grey sea throwing up spray in the marina, and thundering relentlessly on to the beach. Her eyes searched for some sign of the cruiser, her ears attuned for any sound that would tell her Colt was coming back.

And then she heard it: the nerve-jarring siren of an ambulance on the far side of the bay. She couldn't see a thing, because the mist was too thick now, but without another thought she was running out of the office and down the stairs—not bothering to wait for the lift—surprising the security guard as she tore past him and out to her car.

Had Colt found Tim? Had it been him summoning the ambulance from the cruiser? Or was it answering a message the lifeboat had sent from somewhere out there on the cruel, fathomless sea?

Turning the ignition, her blood ran cold as she considered what it could mean if the latter were the case. Perhaps the *Cassandra* had run into difficulties. Perhaps both Colt and Tim . . .

She stifled a small sob and tried to shake herself out of such negative thinking, keeping her concentration fully on the road. And now, as she rounded a corner, she could see the flashing light of the ambulance near the jetty. The lifeboat was in, too, and she gave a little cry of relief to see the cruiser floating alongside of it.

*Oh, Colt!* Tears stung her eyes and she brushed at them impatiently, pressing her foot down harder on the accelerator. So Colt was safe. Thank God! But was Tim injured or . . . worse? Was that why they had sent for an ambulance? Or was it just a precautionary step in situations like these?

She couldn't bear to think what the answers might be, and she had to stifle another small sob, sending up a silent prayer. *Please let everything be all right!*

Bringing her car to an abrupt halt just past the ambulance, she jumped out and ran back, pushing her way through the crowd that was gathering to see what was happening.

'What is it? What's happened?' She fought her way through the curious onlookers, looking hopelessly from the ambulance-man climbing into his cab to the wind-rocked *Cassandra* beside the jetty for some sign of Colt. 'Tell me what's happened! I'm a relative!' She was grabbing the sleeve of a passing coastguard, her face flushed from running, her eyes anxious and wide. 'Where's Mr Falloner? Tell me!'

Beneath the dark sou'wester, the man's weather-beaten face was grim. 'There's been a near-tragic accident. I'm afraid Mr Falloner's in a bad way.'

Raine blanched, tugging her wind-blown hair back out of her eyes. And, as the thought darted through her mind, urgently she was demanding, '*Which* Mr Falloner?'

But the man was hurrying off towards the lifeboat, obviously having more important things to do than talk to her. And, as the ambulance suddenly sped away, Raine stood looking anxiously about her, feeling sick and alone.

He'd meant Tim, of course, logic surfaced to assure her. Not that she wanted any harm to have come to him, either, she thought, fearfully. But the man said near-tragic. So he was still alive. But where was Colt? In the ambulance with his brother? Oh, God! Why couldn't she find him? she wondered, frantically looking around.

'Colt!' She was desperate to find him, was running towards the lifeboat, her hard, ragged breathing hurting her lungs. Perhaps he was with the coastguard. Why wasn't there anyone to ask? And then a strong hand was on her arm, stalling her.

She swung round, staring up at the tall man with a mixture of relief and disappointment in her face.

'Jack! What's happened?' At least *he'd* talk to her! she realised gratefully, too distraught even to query what Jack Hardwicke was doing there.

'Timothy Falloner's dinghy broke up on the rocks,' he elucidated, and, seeing the colour draining out of Raine's cheeks, added quickly, 'But he's going to be all right. Don't worry.'

'And Colt?' Raine quizzed, breathing relief that Tim's condition wasn't as serious as she'd feared. 'Where's Colt? I have to see him.'

As she made to move instinctively towards the jetty, she felt Jack's arm restraining her.

She looked at him questioningly. 'What's wrong?' she asked, holding her breath, her eyes two dark pools of anxiety as she noticed the grave expression in his.

'I'm afraid he's hurt, Raine . . . quite badly,' Jack told her hesitantly. 'That's why they sent for the ambulance to be here when we came in.'

'No.' It was a whispered denial, her blood seeming to trickle out of her like a lifestream, leaving her weak and cold. The

sound of a car door slamming, the buffeting wind and the
fading voices of the dispersing crowd didn't seem like part of
her world as her senses returned enough for her to ask, 'How?
How was he hurt?'

'Saving his brother.' Jack looked down at the wounded
emerald eyes—the only animation in the delicate, pinched
face—and he slid an avuncular arm around Raine's shoulders.
'Timothy was floundering in an impossible current when we
reached him,' he went on, 'and he couldn't reach the lifebelt or
the line we threw him. We couldn't swing any closer to him or
the *Cassandra* would have been dashed to pieces, so Colt dived
in to save him.' There was a deep respect for Colt in Jack
Hardwicke's voice, and in his eyes. 'God knows how he fought
that current and kept his brother afloat as well, but he did.
And Timothy was panicking, too, so that made things more
difficult for him. Anyway, as he brought him back, I managed
to grab Timothy, but then the *Cassandra* rolled and Colt was
hit. He was knocked unconscious and I couldn't reach him. If
the lifeboat hadn't reached us when it did . . .' He shrugged,
swallowing from the thought of what might have transpired
and, as Raine's thoughts followed the same lines, she couldn't
control the tears which, until then, she had been holding back.
Ashamed of them, she cupped her hands over her face, murmuring her apologies to Jack.

So Colt had put his life on the line to save his brother's, in
spite of everything, she realised, filled with admiration for the
man she had married. And if he hadn't been the powerful
swimmer he was . . . if the rescue boat hadn't arrived . . .

She shuddered. 'I must see him,' she said bleakly, finding
her handkerchief and blowing her nose, gathering herself
together.

The man looked down at her, his face concerned. 'Do you
want me to come with you?' he asked gently.

'No. I'll be all right, thanks.' Raine managed a weak smile
for Colt's second-in-command. 'Were you at the office?' she

queried then.

Jack nodded, running a hand over his balding head. 'Colt didn't want anyone else going with him, but I insisted. Under threat of being fired, too.' He grimaced. 'You know, you've got a very stubborn husband there.'

Raine pulled another wan smile. 'Yes, I know,' she accepted. Stubborn, and brave, too. And at that moment all she wanted was to be with him. To tell him how much she admired him for what he had done, how much she cared . . .

'I'm glad you were there,' she uttered to Jack. 'If you hadn't been, Tim might not have survived, either.' Automatically, she looked towards the jetty. 'Where is he?' she asked frowning. 'If the ambulance came for Colt . . .'

'Tim went with him.' Jack put up a reassuring hand when he saw her frown deepen. 'He'll be all right, though,' he told her again, his deprecating tone making it obvious that he considered Tim had put everyone to a great deal of trouble and risk. 'I shouldn't think he'll be suffering from very much more than shock.'

He wasn't. The hospital confirmed it as soon as Raine arrived, but told her that Colt was still being treated.

'There are some chairs outside his room,' a young nurse said pleasantly to her. 'You can wait there if you like, until the doctor says it's all right for you to go in.'

Raine thanked her, firstly telephoning Ruth from the nearest pay phone to keep her informed. Then, from the nurse's directions, she followed a maze of corridors until she found the private ward where Colt had been taken, flopping down on one of the chairs outside.

How badly was he hurt? The thought kept whirring round her brain, because no one she had asked in reception had seemed to know, and she glanced up quickly as a white-coated doctor came out of the room opposite. He seemed not to notice her sitting there, however, and hurried off, his footsteps echoing back along the highly polished corridor. Raine stared after him, wondering if that sense of urgency about him meant that Colt's condition was critical.

*Oh, God, let him be all right!* she implored with every fragment of her love for him, and vowed that as soon as she could talk to him she would tell him of that love. Over the past hour or so, she had tried imagining what it would be like living without him, and couldn't bear to think of the empty, meaningless existence such a future would hold. And suddenly she was crying again—quietly and very privately—until a nurse came out and told her that she could go in.

When she did, Colt's appearance came as a shock to her. He was sitting on the edge of the bed—not unconscious as she'd imagined, but very much awake—one long leg dangling, the other outstretched to the floor, pulling a dark blue hospital robe over a heavily bandaged chest, and he was alone. Raine saw him wince as he moved too adventurously, his pain instantly concealed behind a cool mask as he looked up and saw her.

Neither of them spoke for a moment—their eyes locking—and Raine felt a nervous contraction in her stomach. 'I—I was worried about you,' she said, somewhat breathlessly then.

'Were you?' His expression was as sceptical as his tone, a response which sent a cutting arrow through Raine's heart.

'Jack . . . and the lifeboatman . . . they said you were in a bad way,' she breathed, relief on seeing that he wasn't making her limbs feel like jelly.

Almost, it seemed, he sensed the relief in her, and an eyebrow arched in apparent surprise, although he made no comment. 'I was probably out cold when Jack saw me last,' he told her coolly, fastening the belt of his robe with hands that were remarkably more steady than hers felt. 'And are you sure the lifeboatman wasn't talking about Tim?' He was looking at her intently, as though for some sign of response. 'He was pretty hysterical when I pulled him away from the sorry mess of that dinghy.'

Imagining how frightening it must have been out there in the water, Raine shivered, gripping the back of the padded chair beside the bed. The room smelt typically of hospital, clean and clinical, the bed linen starched white against the cold sterility of the pale green walls.

'That was a very brave thing to do.' A lump came to her throat, making her voice crack, and she felt Colt's eyes on her still—steady and unwavering.

'Have you seen Tim?' There was no hint of any emotion in the deep voice, and Raine shook her head. All she had been concerned with was how Colt was, she thought torturedly, but she couldn't tell him that, feeling somehow as though she were facing a stranger.

'Are you all right?' she asked suddenly, noticing how he winced again as he leaned back against the mountain of pillows.

He grimaced, but for his bandages, looking as strong and physically powerful as ever. 'I don't think I'm likely to die from a small bump on the head and a few fractured ribs,' he stated drily. 'Yes, I'm perfectly all right . . . which I think is more than can be said about you.' His gaze was running over her windswept hair, her rather puffy eyes and her pale cheeks—still blotchy from crying—and with a line between his brows, he said censuringly, 'You look awful.'

'Thanks,' Raine responded flatly, detecting concern in him for her despite his own injuries, although there was no trace of any warmth behind it. She remembered how, that time she had been nursing Sean, Colt had asked if she'd give him as much comfort if he were sick, and she wanted to, desperately. To cry out that she'd thought she would die during those moments when she'd dreaded that he might not come back. But all the things she had promised herself she would tell him when she'd been waiting to see him remained unsaid, frozen by the icy barriers which seemed impenetrable between them.

'We can't go on like this,' he said suddenly, on a sharp

intake of breath.

Raine looked at him quickly. 'What do you mean?' she queried, swallowing, and dropped down on to the wooden arm of the chair, because she already knew what he meant.

His mouth was grim as he scanned her troubled features. 'I only have to look at you to see what I'm doing to you . . . what we're doing to each other,' he said with immense disparagement, and she guessed that it was his injuries that made him draw another quick breath. 'Neither of us can deny that it's been wrong from the beginning,' he was admitting, his words seeming to stem the flow of blood pumping through Raine's arteries. 'I'm not blaming you for anything,' he said dispassionately, his expression shuttered as he looked down at her where she sat, pale and speechless and numb. 'It's probably all my fault, rushing you into marrying me as I did.' His mouth tugged down in self-deprecation. 'And for purely selfish reasons,' he added, his frank admission piercing her to the heart. His eyes ran over her again, over her face and the smooth column of her throat, to the perfection of her body beneath the unflattering sweater and jeans, as though he were trying to imprint her image on his mind before he finally let her go. She couldn't help noticing how tired he looked, absently reminding herself of the ordeal he had been through. 'When I get out of here,' he said quietly, his eyes lifting to hers, 'we're going to have to do something about it.'

A thin thread of pain started to uncoil inside of her. She knew what he was saying, even though, from the beginning, she'd nursed the slimmest hope that there could be some sort of future for them together. But, of course, there couldn't be. Marrying her had been a demonstration by Colt of victory over his brother, retribution for Tim's taking Stephanie. Now that he had seen how genuine Tim's guilt was, how he had practically tried to drown himself because of it, that need for revenge must surely have been torn out of him when he'd been out there fighting to save his brother's life. Which left her,

Raine, where? As no more than a useless pawn in his life—unnecessary to him now.

Well, at least he'd never know of her foolish love for him, she thought with a torturous attempt at detachment as she stood up.

'Yes,' she responded, almost inaudibly, and was glad a nurse came in at that moment to announce that Ruth Falloner was outside. She took her mother-in-law's arrival as an opportunity to get away from him, so that he wouldn't see just how her heart was breaking.

# CHAPTER TEN

RAINE came out of the house as the last of the cows was leaving the milking-shed, and she offered a wan smile to the tall man who was washing down the yard. 'All done, Dad?'

He nodded and stood up, leaning on his broom to look at his daughter. In the soft check shirt, blue denims and wellington boots, she presented a thinner, paler figure than the one he had escorted down the aisle only a month before, and he shook his head in disapproval. 'Have you had a proper breakfast this morning?' he quizzed, his brows knitted in concern.

Raine uttered a small sound of confirmation, hoping that he wouldn't check with her mother and discover exactly how little she had eaten again.

But the truth was, she had no appetite these days. And looking around her, she wondered why the familiarity of the grey stone buildings and gently sloping pastures, the smell of her mother's cooking and Nick's tuneful whistling, could do nothing to ease the pain in her heart which, with every day that passed, seemed to grow worse instead of better.

Picking up an empty pail and trudging purposefully across the yard, Raine tried not to think, but despairingly she knew that nothing—not even hard, physical work—could drive Colt out of her mind. And it had been the same for the past ten days. She had worn herself out—mentally and physically—in a vain attempt to forget him; tossed and turned each night in an agony of longing. And the need for him was becoming more and more unbearable, she thought hopelessly, so wrapped up in her misery she wasn't even aware of her father's farmhand breaking off his whistling to call 'good morning' to her.

Instead of filling her bucket when she reached the tap, she set it down and slipped around to the back of the barn, so that no one would see the tears which were suddenly stinging her lids.

The fact was that she hadn't spoken to Colt in private again after that morning at the hosiptal, since Ruth had been staying with them. During that weekend, after he had come home, his ice-cold civility towards her, Raine, had only reinforced what she had already known—that everything was over between them. Anguish gripped her chest like a vice as she recalled his cold indifference towards her, yet, leaning back against the barn wall with her hands clenched at her sides, her eyes shut fast against her tears, she wondered with a hopeless despera-tion how he was. He had been in pain, she was sure, that last morning when he'd insisted on driving himself to the office, although it had been beyond his pride to let her know it. Just as she'd been sure enough of his reasons for suggesting that Ruth took Sean to England for a few days, so that, after they had gone that day, Raine had packed her own belongings and left, only an hour or so before Colt was due back.

She blenched as she recalled it now, hating herself for sneaking away as she had—too cowardly to face the ultimate goodbye from him—and wondering, as she had then, and every day since, how he would explain her absence to Sean. She wondered, too, what Colt must have thought himself when he'd come home that day and discovered that she'd gone, nursing agony upon agony to realise that he'd probably consider he'd been let off the hook lightly. For, in the brief note she'd left him, she'd stated that she wouldn't contest a divorce, that she'd expect nothing from him. And she'd had nothing, she thought torturedly now. Not even a telephone call.

Swallowing emotion with a great effort of will, she squared her slender shoulders and, staring out at the blue water beyond the emerald fields, steeled herself to go back to her chores, trying to impress upon herself that it was useless mooning over a man who didn't want her. She had to get over this agonising love for him or go insane, she told herself firmly. They could never have been right for each other. But as she came back into the yard and saw the postman's van just pulling out of the gate, her heart leaped in reckless anticipation. Surely today there might be a letter?

Breath held, she saw Nick Chalmers' stalwart figure crossing the wet flagstones, wondered absently why his dark good looks and his obvious interest in her over the years had never stirred her to have more than a casual date with him, or produced the devastating desire in her that Colt's had. But all she could take in now was the white envelope he was holding out to her.

'It's for you, bright eyes,' he grinned, and whether it was because of the way her fingers trembled as she took it from his mud-stained hands, or the sudden flush to her cheeks, she wasn't sure, but something prompted him to ask, 'Is everything all right?'

As far as Nick was concerned, Raine was simply taking a short break alone, and if he thought it odd that she should be doing so so soon after her wedding, he hadn't expressed as much.

'Perfectly, thanks.' She even managed a smile to assure him everything was, but her hand was shaking as she turned the envelope over, and she wasn't even aware of Nick walking away.

Disappointment came like a knife in her chest. It wasn't from Colt. It was from somewhere abroad, but the Jersey address had been crossed through and redirected to the farm in her husband's own flowing scrawl, and that cold, indifferent gesture on his part tore at her heart.

How could he? she wondered with soul-rending anguish at realising how little she meant to him, and she had to force back an upsurge of fresh emotion as she opened the letter.

'Raine! He did it! I'm on my honeymoon!' Her friend's

enthusiasm leaped up at her from the page. 'I think Dave was afraid I'd change my mind, so here we are in Venice. Now I know I'm going to be as happy as you are. C.'

Though pleasantly surprised, Raine found it an effort not to break down completely when she read that last comment. But she didn't, stifling her own sorrows and silently wishing her friend all the joy she herself hadn't known with Colt.

'Who is it from?'

Shielding her eyes from the bright sunlight, she looked up, startled to see her father watching her.

'From Colette,' was all she could manage, folding the letter away, but try though she did she couldn't hide her disappointment from him, the tremor in her voice.

John Welland viewed his daughter with some scepticism. 'Don't you think you ought to contact him? Make some effort to try and make a go of things . . .'

He broke off as Raine shook her head, and she saw him shake his, but in exasperation.

He blamed her for the break-up of the relationship this time, she was sure of that. When she'd arrived over a week ago—pale and subdued, with nowhere else to go—and told them that her marriage was over, she remembered her mother had cried. She'd despised herself then for bringing her troubles home to them again, although she knew it wasn't a thing she could have kept from them for long. But the way John Welland had suggested that Colt was mature enough to know what he was doing when he married her, that he didn't seem the type to take his marriage vows lightly, strongly implied that her father was on *his* side, that he thought his daughter fickle, and, since she couldn't bear to tell him or her mother the humiliating truth of why Colt had married her, she was resigned to letting them go on thinking so.

'Your mother and I are going over to the Yates' place to look at a couple of heifers this morning,' the man's voice broke through her tormented thoughts. 'Would you like to come?'

Raine shook her head again, a few strands of hair coming loose from the clasp at the nape of her neck. 'No, thanks, Dad. I think I'll stay here,' she answered dispiritedly, unable to face the awkward questions which she knew her presence would raise with their neighbours.

Her father shrugged and trudged away, and a few minutes later she heard the car pull away from the front of the house.

When they had gone, the place seemed intolerably empty. Nick had taken the tractor down to the lower meadow, and suddenly Raine felt crushingly alone. There was nothing to do inside the house, since Joan Welland was a very methodical and fastidious housekeeper, and, with everything under control at the moment where the farm was concerned, Raine was at a loss as to what to do. Loneliness seemed to crowd in around her, and in a moment of panic she wondered whether she'd been unwise not going with her parents to the Yates'.

Well, it was too late to regret it now, she thought, self-chasteningly; stuffing her hands into the pockets of her jeans, she strolled off in the direction of the fields.

The morning was warm, with a fresh breeze coming off the sea, and as she wandered down through the first gate she could taste the tang of salt on her lips. The cows were grazing peacefully as she ambled past them, tugging at the tender green shoots. One lowed, and another answered, and on the sweet, summer air came the distant sound of the tractor in the lower pasture.

Or was it? If she hadn't known better, she would have sworn the sound came from the yard, but she was too engrossed in her misery to question it, unable to stop torturing herself with thoughts of Colt.

Why? Oh, why had he married her? she reasoned tormentedly, when he'd known she'd only wind up getting hurt. Had he cared so little for her that he could use her and then discard her so cruelly? It was agony to believe that he had, but she knew she had to face up to that fact. She thrust her hands deeper into her pockets, numb to the warming sunshine and the sweet scents of the meadow. How could she have been so gullible not to realise what his motives were when he'd asked her to marry him? she thought bitterly. Yet he'd been so tender that night—such an unbelievable lover—how could she have known that it was purely a physical thing with him, that he hadn't felt anything for her at all?

Well, she had paid the price for her naïvete, she told herself with a heart-twisting acceptance, and it was all behind her now. And, with a firm determination, she decided there and then that in a day or two she would start looking for a secretarial post in England. She wouldn't be a burden to her parents any longer, and at least on the mainland she'd be far enough away from Colt to be certain of never seeing him again, she thought achingly, biting her lower lip. And this time, when she tasted salt, she knew that it wasn't just from the wind coming off the sea.

Hearing the vehicle pull up behind the gate, she swung round, realising through a blur of tears that it wasn't the tractor but a Land Rover she'd heard. She froze, recognising the familiar figure who had jumped down from it and was coming through the gate, striding purposefully towards her.

'Colt!' His name left her lips on a whisper, and she stood as if rooted, too stunned for a moment to move. Then, aware that she had been crying, unable to face the humiliation of his seeing her like this and perhaps guessing why, she swung away from him.

'Raine!' His urgent command stopped her in her tracks, although she didn't turn around.

'W-what do you want?' she asked tremulously, because he was right behind her now, and she was battling against an overwhelming compulsion to turn into his arms.

'To talk to you.' There was soft persuasion in his voice which made her catch her breath, and she tried not to remember how those deep, rich tones could drive her mindless for him.

She took a deep breath, praying for strength to conduct this interview with him with some degree of dignity. 'What about?' she asked, without looking at him. But her voice shook and, half angrily, she said through tears that wouldn't be restrained, 'I told you in my note that I wouldn't contest a divorce. Why did you have to come here?'

She stared down at the ground, seeing only a blur of emerald and purple where the clover mingled with the grass, and heard Colt say rather impatiently, 'Raine . . . look at me.'

She didn't want to, but there was a determination in his voice that couldn't be ignored, and reluctantly she obeyed.

He looked thinner beneath the light cotton shirt and dark cords he was wearing, and she noticed how his skin appeared to be stretched across his cheekbones, which, with the tired lines around his eyes, lent him an almost gaunt look. Absently, she wondered if he had been worrying about Tim.

'I haven't come here to talk about a divorce,' he said, almost gently, his eyes fixed intently on her soft, wan features. 'I came here to . . . to ask you to come back.'

A small spark of hope leaped inside of her. 'Why?' she queried in a trembling voice, her eyes suspicious, and the little flame died as she considered that there could be any number of reasons for his wanting her back. Like Sean, for one. But the thought of the little boy brought a lump to her throat, and to hide her emotion she said brittly, 'Why, Colt? Afraid Tim will have the last laugh if he finds out we've split up?'

Anger darkened his eyes. Or *was* it anger? she thought wonderingly. He looked almost in pain, and he was flinging back in a voice raw with some emotion she couldn't begin to understand, 'Why can't you just for once learn to trust my motives?'

He turned on his heel and was striding away from her, his hands thrust deep into his trouser pockets, and a sick, chilling emptiness spread through her. A sob caught in her throat, and she turned away so that she wouldn't see him leave, realising that she would have been prepared to go back with him for whatever reason he had wanted her to. Anything would have been better than this endless, agonising torture without him. But now, because of that stupid, stupid comment, it was too late.

She heard him slam the door of the Land Rover, braced herself as she waited for it to pull away. Then suddenly she heard him speak her name and she pivoted round, her heart leaping. He hadn't left, after all! He'd come back!

She looked at him, puzzled by the dark emotion in his eyes, and even more by the golden, fawnlike little creature he was holding in his arms.

'I know it's the bride who gives the calf, but I'm breaking with tradition,' he said drily, coming towards her, 'although the meaning's still the same. I want to share life with you, Raine. All of it. Create new with our children . . .'

He broke off, his voice cracking in some mysterious way. Stunned, she didn't even realise that she was taking the animal from him until she felt its warm body against her own. And suddenly she was sobbing, cradling it to her, anguish pouring out of her in hot tears on to the creature's soft head.

'Oh, my beautiful, beautiful love, don't cry.' There was a rough intensity in Colt's voice, and his embrace was crushing, his lips raining kisses into the soft silk of her hair.

She couldn't understand why he was doing this, saying these things, breaking her heart when his own was so devoid of any real feeling for her, but at that moment she didn't care. All she wanted was to be in his arms. To have that clean, familiar scent of him filling her lungs. But, stifled, the calf was beginning to struggle, and Colt drew back a little so that Raine could let it go.

Wriggling free on long, spindly legs, the animal gave a little snort of indignation, shook itself, and then trotted off as Colt pulled Raine back into his arms.

'When I came home and found you'd gone, I almost went out of my mind,' he whispered hoarsely, holding her so tightly that it hurt. She gave a small groan, her body melting against his. During the past ten days, when she'd thought she would never feel his arms around her again, she had ached for this. Only, now it was real. He was here. But she still couldn't understand why—why he was holding her as if he would never let her go.

'But it was what you wanted,' she accused, puzzlingly, pushing away from him just enough to look up at him with dark, tortured eyes. 'In the hospital, you said——'

'I know what I said,' he cut in, self-censuringly, 'but I didn't think you'd go . . . just like that . . . that you'd leave me. I was just so angry still . . . sick at myself . . . but over that weekend I decided that what we needed was a few days alone to try and sort things out. Why do you think I asked Ruth to take Sean back to England with her?'

Raine couldn't grasp what he was saying. 'But I thought . . .' She lifted her head, her eyes scanning the pained lines and angles of his face. 'I thought you wanted me to leave . . . that you didn't want me there any more. Anyway, I couldn't have gone on being just a symbol of victory over your brother.'

The wind ruffled his hair, and he raked it back from his forehead, staring down at her incredulously. 'Do you honestly, really still believe that?'

Raine looked up at him, biting her lower lip, not sure *what* she believed any more. Overhead, she heard a plover cry, caught the distant drone of Nick's tractor somewhere in the lower fields.

'But I heard you,' she reminded him, pain stabbing her as she recalled his conversation with Tim in the study that day.

Colt's hands slid down to her elbows, their warmth burning through her thin, check shirt. 'What you heard was a purely facetious comment,' he told her, yet she still wasn't sure what he meant. 'Tim accused me of marrying you to get even with him, and I was simply agreeing with him.' And, seeing the wounded expression on her face, he said, rather impatiently, 'For God's sake, Raine! If you'd stayed at that door a few moments longer, you'd have heard me telling him how I'd never listened to anything so conceited in my life! That I'd hardly have wasted valuable time working out a plan solely for revenge on him. And if I'd wanted that—which I didn't——' he interjected drily, with a grimace '—I certainly wouldn't have been prepared to jeopardise *your* future—or my own—to achieve it.'

Raine stared at him, her eyes brilliant from the mixed emotions suddenly pulsing through her. 'But you asked me to live with you first,' she murmured, still unsure of him. 'You wouldn't have married me if I'd agreed to . . .'

'Not at first . . . not right away,' he admitted, and very gently he took her hands and drew her down to sit beside him on the warm grass. 'Only because I didn't want to rush you into something you weren't ready for,' he told her then, 'and I wanted you so much that I didn't want to do or say anything that would have frightened you off. After the way I'd treated you over Tim, when you weren't even to blame, I thought I'd probably already ruined my chances where any relationship with you was concerned. I knew I had to let things ride . . . take things gently with you for a while to get you to even *like* me again, and I fully intended to do that.' His mouth pulled down one side. 'When I found out, though, that Tim had been phoning you, and I asked you what your feelings were about him, you didn't want to talk about them, and I thought that deep down you still loved him . . . that if I waited, he'd persuade you to go back to him again. I knew I was rushing you even by asking you to live with me, but I knew that wouldn't seem so impetuous as asking you to marry me right away. When you refused, though, I'm afraid I panicked. I just couldn't take the chance of losing you to Tim . . . or anyone else, for that matter,' he stated with a hard possessiveness that sent a little thrill through her. 'I'm afraid I wanted you too much for too long.'

'What do you mean?' she queried, breathless from the warm tide of emotions flowing through her—because she was still having a job taking in all he was saying. After all, he'd hardly known her long enough to want her for any great length of time.

'When I took you in my arms at that party six years ago,' he elaborated, trailing one finger down the soft line of her cheek, 'I felt as if I'd been hit between the eyes with something. I'd never wanted any woman as much as I wanted you that night.'

'But you ignored me completely afterwards!' she breathed, flabbergasted, a warm desire stirring in her from his touch.

Remembering, Colt smiled, leaning back to rest on an elbow, and Raine thought she saw him wince. 'I know,' he averred. 'But I'd already sensed that you weren't entirely immune to me, and I knew that if I didn't exercise every ounce of control I had, I'd have been wild enough to consider doing something about it . . . like breaking up your engagement . . . anything to have kept you in my arms.'

Raine met his gaze, hers wide and surprised. 'But you loved Stephanie!' she exhaled, puzzled.

'No, Raine,' he said gently. 'Not then.'

The cattle were champing peacefully, the occasional stamp of hooves making a dull sound on the soft turf. A bee droned. And, from a greater distance, came the ceaseless hiss of the sea.

'Then why . . . why were you still with her?' she queried, unable to understand, her face radiant from the realisation that this man might possibly be in love with *her*.

Colt shrugged. 'Purely because of Sean. No other reason,' he explained on a deep sigh. 'Stephanie was a good mother, in spite of everything else . . . and I knew that if I divorced her . . . with my kind of job . . . the hours and the trips abroad . . . the chances were she'd probably have got custody. I was prepared to stay with her solely so that wouldn't happen, and

Stephanie wasn't complaining. She could still have the luxury she was used to and the Falloner name, and carry on with her affairs behind a thoroughly respectable front.' His brow furrowing, he added, almost as an afterthought, 'She couldn't help it, you know, Raine. It was like an illness with her.'

He looked so pained, probably from remembering the anguish of his first marriage, Raine suspected, and she placed a gentle hand on his arm. 'I know,' she said quietly. 'Tim told me.'

Colt looked at her surprised. 'Did he?' His frown deepened. Then, with another sigh, he said, 'Yes . . . the poor fool was certainly made to pay dearly for getting involved.' And, shaking his head, 'They both were.' There was both regret and compassion in the deep tones. 'Anyway,' he went on, sitting up and tearing absently at a stalk of grass, 'I couldn't bring myself to make love to her during that last year or so, even if I'd wanted to and I wasn't too keen about involving myself in extra-marital relationships with other women, believe it or not, Raine.' He looked down at her, their eyes locking and the sincerity, the love, in his made her grow weak. 'I thought I could cope . . . just as long as I had Sean and my work,' he continued, twisting the blade of grass between his fingers, 'but at that party that night, you made me realise—even though it was quite innocently—what I was depriving myself of.' He pulled a wry face, tossed the grass aside and suddenly was gathering her to him. 'I think, if you'd married Tim, I'd have formed a company in the Outer Hebrides and posted you both there, just to keep temptation out of my way,' he stated drily. 'Or at the very least, helped him persuade you to move to England with him as I knew he wanted to do.'

She couldn't comprehend that behind that cool, sophisticated exterior he had harboured such thoughts about her even then, and a little tremor shivered down her spine. 'You hid it well,' she murmured, marvelling at his impeccable reserve.

His mouth compressed. 'What else could I do? You were going to marry Tim, and I respected you both. Then when you jilted him—as I thought,' he corrected on a self-condemnatory note, 'and that dreadful accident happened, I felt like strangling you with my bare hands.'

'I'd noticed,' she uttered wryly, nuzzling against him, suddenly feeling delightfully warm and safe. But as she caught him to her she heard him wince again and sat up, saying worriedly, 'You're in pain. Are your ribs still hurting?'

He gave her a canted smile. 'Only when I move,' he teased, noting with tenderness the concern in her eyes. And then he brushed the subject aside to say gently, 'Do you know when I first realised I was in love with you?' And, when she shook her head, 'When we were in the car, leaving Ruth's, and I realised that all along, in spite of the way I'd treated you, you'd been protecting my feelings by not telling me the truth about Stephanie and Tim. That's why I wasn't showering you with apologies as I should have been . . . I was much too shaken by the way I felt. Consequently, I couldn't believe my luck when you agreed to marry me,' he breathed against her hair, his fingers entwining in its softness until it came loose from its clasp. 'Then, when you accused me of marrying you to get even with Tim, I just couldn't believe that you could mistrust me so much. And the worst thing was I knew it was probably all my own fault, because of the way I'd treated you in the beginning.'

'But why didn't you tell me then that you hadn't been serious about what you'd said to Tim?' she asked, baffled, delighting in the warmth of his body, the full, comforting strength of him. 'Why couldn't you just tell me the truth?'

He shrugged. 'Pride, I suppose,' he admitted with a self-censuring grimace. 'Every time I tried to explain, you didn't want to listen, and I was angry with you for thinking what you did.'

And she hadn't wanted to listen, she could accept now,

because she'd been too ready to believe the worst about him. Oh, what a stupid, stupid fool she'd been!

'That night when I walked out . . . when I found you with Tim . . .' His voice was ragged with emotion. 'I spent the night in a hotel room just thinking . . . wondering how I could come back and make you love me. Then, when you left that day, I thought I'd lost all chance of that for good.'

And she'd thought he'd been with Jocelyn Day!

'But I do love you! I've always loved you!' she admitted openly now, pulling away from his fierce embrace to look with shining eyes into his strong and very dear features. 'Why do you think I wouldn't just live with you when you asked me to? Because I didn't think I could bear it if you ever ended our affair. That's why sometimes I let you go on thinking what you did about my feelings for Tim . . . because I was so scared of how I felt about you . . . because I thought you didn't care anything for me.'

'Oh, Raine!' Her name was torn from him as he held her against him. 'If you only knew how much. And I think I was only ready to believe that there was something going on between you and Tim because I didn't want to accept that the reason you'd turned against me was primarily all my own doing. Incidentally, Tim made sure of putting me straight about the two of you last week before he went to London. He came to see me to tell me he's got a flat and a new job there, so with luck he'll be back on his feet again pretty soon.' Raine noticed the element of relief in his voice as he related this about his brother, and then suddenly he was getting up and drawing her gently to her feet.

'What about you? Us?' he asked softly, caressing her cheek lovingly with the back of one strong, warm hand. 'I've spent ten days trying to convince myself that, if I came to you, you wouldn't send me away again. Well, darling?' He shot a glance down the field to where the calf was prancing skittishly among the darker-coated heifers. 'Are you going to accept my offering?'

Her gaze following the direction of his, Raine looked up at him, at the strong, proud lines of his face, at the sunlight streaking fire through his hair, and her eyes shone with the depth of her emotion for him. 'What do you think?' she murmured with a soft, yielding smile.

Colt's eyes were dark and smouldering as they flicked from the deserted farmhouse to meet hers again. 'Prove it to me,' he whispered, a smile tugging at his own mouth.

A small dart of excitement shot through her. 'Now?' she breathed, surprised, her heart giving a little flutter, tingeing her cheeks pink, as she realised what he meant.

'Now.'

'But we can't . . . I mean . . . your ribs . . .'

'Now,' he commanded softly, though his tone left no room for argument.

Her smile trembled, and her body started to tingle with anticipation. Then, with a helpless little shrug, she turned and led him obediently back to the house.

A long time later, Raine lay with her head in the curve of her husband's shoulder, warm and content and fulfilled. It had been perfect, their lovemaking. A blending of minds and bodies that had brought them an ecstasy that she knew was beyond anything either of them had experienced before. And drowsily she thought of all the years ahead of them when they would share the same rapture, other joys, children, and perhaps a few problems, she mused, reasoning, although she knew that they could cope with anything, together, secure in the knowledge of each other's love.

Outside, the cattle lowed softly in the morning sunshine and, remembering, she wondered with some amusement what her father would say when he returned and found a little Jersey calf frolicking among his Guernseys. Well, explanations could come later, she decided dreamily, nestling closer to Colt, but he stirred and, raising himself up on an elbow, looked down into her radiant, flushed face.

'I thought you were asleep,' he whispered, and, brushing a gentle thumb across her lips, asked solicitously, 'Was it satisfactory?'

He knew it was, but she smiled up at him, reading the dark desire in his eyes and feeling a mutual response in herself as he feathered kisses over the pale ivory of her throat and shoulders.

'Mmm,' she murmured, her breath catching as his touch brought a new hunger for him pulsing through her again. 'Not bad.' And, in the moment before passion had her surrendering to him completely, she uttered teasingly, 'For a man with broken ribs!'

## Harlequin Temptation dares to be different!

Once in a while, we Temptation editors spot a romance that's truly innovative. To make sure *you* don't miss any one of these outstanding selections, we'll mark them for you.

**EDITOR'S CHOICE**

When the "Editors' Choice" fold-back appears on a Temptation cover, you'll know we've found that extra-special page-turner!

THE

*Temptation*

EDITORS

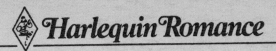

## Coming Next Month

### 2959 PAINTED LADY Diana Hamilton

Ziggy, reunited with her grandfather in England, revises her opinion of him and the family feud that separated them. But she won't change her opinion of Rafe d'Anjou. She's sure his interest in bringing her and her grandfather together, and in herself, is entirely selfish.

### 2960 ONLY MY DREAMS Rowan Kirby

A true romantic and dreamer, Erinna is furious when her staid Midlands tutor, Dr. John Bryce, cautions her against taking life at face value. What does he know, she fumes, a man seemingly impervious to any real emotion himself!

### 2961 ALWAYS A BRIDESMAID Patricia Knoll

Shelby Featherstone wants store space in A. J. Court's exclusive San Diego mall—not a ring on her finger. And especially not the heartache of having to plan his real fiancée's wedding!

### 2962 STORM CLOUDS GATHERING Edwina Shore

Everyone is keen to tell Jenna that Drew Merrick is back on the Australian island where they both grew up—but nobody can tell her why. Certainly it's the last thing Jenna needs just when she's made up her mind to marry Adam.

### 2963 YESTERDAY'S ENEMY Lee Stafford

Ten years ago Steve Rodriguez had deprived Nicole's stepfather of his livelihood, so it's ironic when her job lands her back at the scene of the crime. Will Steve recognize her as "young Nicky"? And if he does, how should she react?

### 2964 WITHOUT LOVE Jessica Steele

Kassia lost her job because of Lyon Mulholland, who even blocked her subsequent efforts to get another one. So her feelings for him bordered on hatred. Yet when he makes handsome amends, she finds her troubles are only just starting....

Available in February wherever paperback books are sold, or through Harlequin Reader Service:

In the U.S.
901 Fuhrmann Blvd.
P.O. Box 1397
Buffalo, N.Y. 14240-1397

In Canada
P.O. Box 603
Fort Erie, Ontario
L2A 5X3

 *Harlequin Books*

You're never too young to enjoy romance. Harlequin for you . . . and Keepsake, young-adult romances destined to win hearts, for your daughter.

Pick one up today and start your daughter on her journey into the wonderful world of romance.

Two new titles to choose from each month.